THE EARTH'S STORY

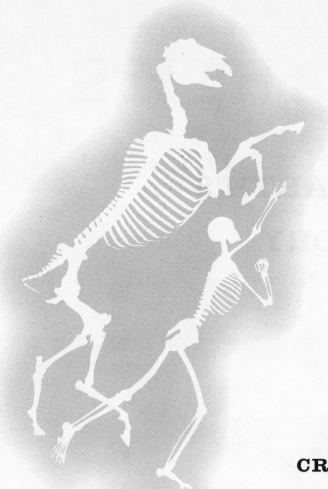

CREATIVE SCIENCE SERIES

Etta Schneider Ress, Ed.D., *editor-in-chief*
Gerhard Ramberg, *art editor*

PLANETS, STARS AND SPACE

Joseph Miles Chamberlain, Chief Astronomer
American Museum-Hayden Planetarium
Thomas D. Nicholson, Associate Astronomer

THE EARTH'S STORY

Gerald Ames and Rose Wyler
Authors, *The Golden Book of Astronomy, Restless Earth,
The Story of the Ice Age*

THE WAY OF THE WEATHER

Jerome Spar, Ph.D., Associate Professor
Department of Meteorology and Oceanography
New York University, N. Y.

ATOMS, ENERGY AND MACHINES

Jack McCormick, Ph.D.
The American Museum of Natural History, New York, N. Y.

THE EARTH'S STORY

by

Gerald Ames & Rose Wyler

In Co-operation with

THE AMERICAN MUSEUM OF NATURAL HISTORY

NEW YORK

Published by Creative Educational Society

1961
Printing

Books by Gerald Ames and Rose Wyler

RESTLESS EARTH

THE STORY OF THE ICE AGE

LIFE ON THE EARTH

THE GOLDEN BOOK OF ASTRONOMY

THE EARTH'S STORY

Copyright 1957 by
Creative Educational Society, Inc.
Mankato, Minnesota

*International copyrights
reserved in all countries*

PRINTED IN THE U.S.A.

Library of Congress Catalog Card Number 57-5976

Foreword

THE POET may speak of the changeless hills, and indeed one man in a lifetime sees no change, but the geologist knows that even mountains are transient forms. Rivers and streams tend to erode the land surface of the earth to a featureless plain sloping gently to the sea. Fortunately for our appreciation of scenery, this tendency is counteracted by geological processes and events which raise plateaus and mountains, which build mighty volcanoes and extensive lava fields, which carve deep glacial troughs and spread thick sheets of ice-borne material over the land. We see one frame of a moving picture which extends hundreds of millions of years into the past.

The pictures and text in this book illustrate the major features of this moving picture as we observe them today. These features are the clues by which the geologist reconstructs the earth's story. The cliffs of the Grand Canyon were originally the sands and muds of an old sea floor. The waste eroded from these cliffs is carried to the Gulf of California, there to form thick sheets of sediment destined to make yet another landmass, perhaps a mountain chain as magnificent as the Rockies or the Himalayas. The rhythm of the inanimate world has its counterpart in the organic world; family upon family of plants and animals has evolved, enjoyed brief supremacy, and later declined or disappeared from the earth.

Foreword (continued)

Besides its philosophical and cultural aspects, geology has close ties with technology and the arts. Our world today depends on ample supplies of mineral raw materials of many kinds, from iron ore, oil, and coal to rare metals like titanium, beryllium, and zirconium. Discovery and exploitation of these raw materials requires the cooperation of the geologist with the mining engineer, the industrialist and the government.

But geology is not an esoteric mystery reserved to the highly trained professional. In no other science has the amateur observer contributed so much. The features of geology are all around us. Deciphering and understanding these features can be a pleasure and an intellectual exercise to any intelligent person. This book provides many of the basic data of geology in an interesting and provocative way—may it stimulate many to read "the story of rocks" as it is unfolded before us, at home and on our travels.

BRIAN H. MASON
Curator of Physical Geology and Mineralogy
The American Museum of Natural History

Contents

Contents (continued)

Part One ∽ ∽ ∽

THE
EVER CHANGING
LAND

THE EVER CHANGING LAND

Because the sun warms the earth's air unevenly in different regions, winds are set into
motion and stream over the globe. Lifting moisture from the sea, they drop it on the land as
rain or snow.

Rocks crumble under the weather's attack.
Their fragments, in the form of sand, silt, and
clay, are picked up by rivers, which carry the
burden from highlands to lowlands, and thence
to the sea.

Rivers, wind, and ice, at work through the
ages, fret the faces of the continents, gradually
leveling mountains and creating plains. Sometimes these changes destroy the homes of living
things; in other cases they create new footholds
for life. In the pictures that follow, we see how
the land, as it wears down, is shaped into wonderful, ever changing forms.

Photo: Ewing Galloway

THE EARTH'S SHAPE

IN THE PAST FEW YEARS, photographs taken from rockets have shown what no man has yet seen with his own eyes—the curved shape of the earth. Below is a Navy rocket, a Viking, photographed as it blasted off from the Proving Ground at White Sands, New Mexico, a few years ago. The Viking climbed 158 miles above the earth, carrying nearly a half ton of scientific instruments. A camera took several shots. Two of them were put together to make the picture on the right. The view covers about 600,000 square miles of Mexico, Texas, and neighboring states. The horizon shows the true curvature of our planet.

The earth has been shaped by a mighty force—its own gravity. Because of the pull between the heavy interior and outer parts of the planet, the surface tends to settle as near the center as possible. As a result, it is held in a curving shape around the center.

Water, pulled by gravity, rests in the great hollows, forming the ocean. Gravity pulls on all parts of the ocean evenly, making the water spread and curve around the earth, as the solid surface does.

Another force works against gravity. This is the pull away from the center—centrifugal force — caused by the earth's rotation. The surface spins fastest around the equator. If it whirled a great deal faster, centrifugal force might fling off water and solid chunks, as mud is flung from a speeding wheel. The actual centrifugal force can't do that, but it does make the earth bulge a little around the equator. Around the poles, where the turning is slow and centrifugal force is weak, the surface has become somewhat flattened. Because of this, the distance through the earth from pole to pole is 26½ miles less than the diameter at the equator.

Photos: courtesy United States Navy

MOUNTAINS AND LOWLANDS

VIEWED FROM SPACE, the earth would seem a watery world, for nearly three-fourths of its surface is ocean-covered. The continents would appear as islands, with surfaces almost as smooth as the sea. Mountains would be like smudges of dirt on a ball. Valleys would be scratches. On a planet nearly 8,000 miles in diameter, the highest peaks are only about twelve miles above the ocean deeps.

Small as they are, compared to the whole earth, these smudges, scratches, and deeps are important. They mark the boundaries within which life can exist. Fishes and other animals range the whole depth of the ocean. On land, the living space is just the surface itself.

Water evaporates from the ocean, and great wind streams carry the moisture over the continents. Falling as rain, it soaks into the soil, where plants take it up. Some water evaporates into the air again, and some runs off in rivers. Gravity, the earth-shaping force, causes the rivers to flow from heights to lowlands, and from lowlands to the sea.

Mountains are cloudmakers. Winds rising on the slope of a range become chilled. This causes the moisture in the air to condense and fall as rain or snow. By the time winds have passed over a mountain chain, they may be so dry that they make a desert of the land over which they pass.

The picture shows Monarch Mountain in the Canadian Rockies. Air and water have been working at the rock faces of the crest, loosening bits of rock, which fall to the slopes and cover them with rubble. Above, the mountain thrusts its rocky hulk to the sky. This rock is the stuff of which the earth's crust is made.

Photo: Georgia Engelhard, Free Lance Photographers Guild

SOIL FROM ROCK

IN MANY PLACES, soil and growing plants spread as far as you can see, without a trace of rock cropping out anywhere. But dig into the soil—a few feet or many—and you are bound to strike rock.

The picture below shows an excavation near Coeburn, Virginia. The men are stripping away soil and rock to uncover a seam of coal. Notice the newly cut bank beyond the shovel. Beneath the cover of soil lies rock partly broken up from the weathering action of water and air. Under this *mantle rock* is unbroken bedrock.

The soil in this place was formed by weathering of the local rock. Metals from the rock combined with oxygen or carbon dioxide from the air and formed new substances. Some of these dissolved in water and were carried away. Part of the rock remained in place as sand and clay.

The Old Man of the Mountain (opposite) was sculptured by weathering of the rock at Franconia Notch, New Hampshire. Legend says the figure inspired Hawthorne to write his story, "The Great Stone Face." The crag is slowly weathering. In time, the Old Man will crumble away, adding to the soil of the slope below.

Photos: courtesy Caterpillar Tractor Company; New Hampshire Planning and Development Commission

MINERALS, THE STUFF OF ROCK

In a piece of granite like that shown on the opposite page, we can see bits of different-colored materials. These are minerals. There are three main kinds in granite. One looks glossy; this is quartz. One is pink or white; this is feldspar. The black mineral is biotite, or black mica.

Like everything else in the world, minerals are composed of atoms. About a hundred kinds of atoms exist in nature. Each kind is an element— a substance that can't be broken down by ordinary chemical means into other substances. Iron, for example, consists of iron atoms and nothing else. The common minerals are compounds of two or more elements. In each mineral the elements are combined in definite proportions. The mineral we use as table salt, for example, is a combination of sodium atoms with chlorine atoms. Their proportion is one to one. If you evaporate salt water, the salt is left behind as a film of tiny crystals. By examining them through a magnifying glass you can see that they are cube-shaped. When a crystal forms, its atoms pull toward each other like magnets. They link in a certain pattern, lining up so regularly that they make a crystal shape with flat sides.

The crystals at the left are quartz, one of the minerals in granite. Quartz forms by the linking of silicon atoms with oxygen atoms. In this specimen the crystals are large and perfect. While they were developing, no other minerals were forming to block their growth. The granite below had a different history. It crystallized from a liquid containing several kinds of atoms and atom groups, which linked into minerals. Those which formed earlier developed well-formed crystals. Others, which formed later, are misshapen because their crystals had to grow in cramped spaces between crystals already there.

Photos: courtesy Ward's Natural Science Establishment; American Museum of Natural History

GRANITE

THESE PORTRAITS of four presidents are sculptured in granite of the Black Hills, South Dakota.

Granite forms deep in the earth's crust. A mass of rock becomes heated—perhaps by radioactivity—and melts. The liquid mass, or *magma*, takes thousands of years to cool, giving plenty of time for large crystals to grow.

Geologists place granite in the class of rocks called *igneous*, meaning "from fire," because it develops from a magma at high temperatures.

Millions of years after its formation, a mass of granite may be uncovered when rocks above it weather and wear away. Today, granite is quarried as a building stone (opposite).

Photos: Joseph Muench (above); Ewing Galloway

SANDSTONE

SANDSTONE is made of quartz grains—sand—held together by a cementing material. Since the grains once were sediments, sandstone is classed as a *sedimentary* rock.

The sandstone in the picture below was deposited a few hundred million years ago. The ripple marks show that the sand which formed it once lay under shallow water, for it was rippled by the motion of waves. The tracks crossing the ripple marks were made by worms.

Perhaps the sand lay on a tidal flat like the one in the picture opposite. The land was slowly sinking. New sediments piled on old. The water around the sand grains contained minerals in solution. These minerals gradually separated from the water, forming a cement that bound the grains.

Later, the floor of the sea rose and became dry land. The sandstone was uncovered, and weathering wore it down. In places, it split between layers, revealing ancient ripple marks.

Today, in some parts of the world, tidal flats are sinking and being buried beneath new layers of sand. Many such deposits will turn into rock. Perhaps, after millions of years, the rock will be exposed, showing ripple marks and traces of creatures that lived in the sand.

Photos: Black Star (opposite); courtesy Smithsonian Institution

SHALE

WHEN GRANITE and similar rocks weather, their fragments may form soil. In this soil are quartz grains, which make sand, and feldspar grains, which make clay. The clay particles are tiny flakes, much smaller than sand grains.

When these mixed materials are blown by wind, or washed away by water, the particles are sorted according to size. A moderate wind will carry away clay dust, leaving sand behind. A stream will transport sand where the current is strong, but where it slackens, the sand is dropped. Clay is carried farther along.

Rivers empty into the sea, where their burden is deposited. Sand and gravel settle near shore. Clay is borne farther out; then it, too, settles. As mud piles up on the sea floor, the weight of the upper layers packs the lower ones tightly. They are cemented by minerals that crystallize out of the water.

Shale, the rock formed from clay minerals, is exposed in many places where old sea beds have become dry land. It has very clear layers, as shown in the rock of the stream bank opposite. Where their edges are weathered, the layers look like sheets of paper piled up. Shale weathers in this way because it is made of flake-shaped minerals.

The piece of shale below has plant fossils in it. Fossils are found only in sedimentary rocks, because burial in sediments helps to preserve plant and animal remains. Igneous rocks form at such high temperatures that any remains of living things would be burned up.

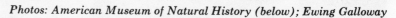

Photos: American Museum of Natural History (below); Ewing Galloway

LIMESTONE

Limestone is made by the chemistry of the sea. One of its elements, the metal calcium, comes from rocks. Water dissolves it from rocks of every land, and rivers carry it to the sea.

The other ingredient is carbonate, made up from carbon dioxide gas. Some of this gas is dissolved from the air; some is given off by the respiration of living things in the sea; and some is released from their dead bodies as a product of decay.

After several steps of chemistry, carbonate is linked with calcium to form calcium carbonate, or "lime." Only a certain amount of calcium carbonate can remain dissolved. When more forms, some of it separates from the water.

Living things play an important role in the creation of limestone. Many kinds of animals and some plants, microscopic and larger, make shells of lime. As they die, their shells pile up in beds on the sea floor. They are pressed together, and calcium carbonate from the water cements them into limestone.

Sometimes the shells remain recognizable, as in the rock shown below. Limestone is quarried for use in making Portland cement and other products (opposite).

Photos: American Museum of Natural History (below); Ewing Galloway

TRANSFORMED ROCKS

A ROCK THAT FORMED near the surface may become deeply buried. Under increasing pressure, it packs tightly together. A nearby magma may heat the rock, and hot fluids may seep into it, dissolving some of its minerals and forming new ones.

Such forces transform, or metamorphose, rocks. Sandstone becomes changed into the hard, sugary-looking rock, quartzite. Shale metamorphoses into slate, and limestone into marble. These are *metamorphic* rocks.

Pulling and shoving forces called stresses are always at work within the crust. When a stress becomes greater than the rock can bear,

the rock gives. It need not break, for pressure helps hold it together. Instead, its crystals split, slip, and regroup, causing a slow, oozing flow. The picture below shows rock that once lay deep in the crust. Although stresses made it crumple, it did not break.

When a rock is under great stress, thin sheets may slide upon one another. Minerals jam together, and each locks with its own kind, forming crystals lined up in sheets. Such arrangements are found in the rocks called schist and gneiss. They tell a story of stresses that pulled the original rock like taffy, changing it into a banded gneiss or a schist.

Photos: courtesy National Museum of Canada (below); American Museum of Natural History

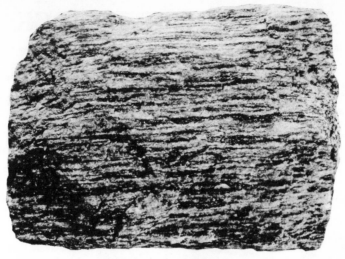

GRANITE GNEISS

SLATE

GNEISS

GRANITE

MICA SCHIST

QUARTZITE

MARBLE

WEATHERING OF ROCK

OLD ROCK FACES, like the gravestone below, have a worn, wasted appearance. This is a result of weathering—the action of atmospheric gases and water. Oxygen and water, for example, join with iron in rocks to form rust particles. These, being soft, are easily carried away.

The picture on the left shows the surface of a granite dome towering above Yosemite Valley, in California. Granite often peels away in sheets—a kind of weathering called exfoliation.

The picture at the right shows weathered rocks in Arizona. Once they formed part of vast, unbroken layers. Air and water crumbled them; streams and wind removed the fragments.

Photos: courtesy U.S. Geological Survey (left); Russ Kinne (below); Joseph Muench (right)

LIMESTONE CAVES

IN FAIRLY WET REGIONS, about two-thirds of the water from rain and snow either flows away or evaporates. The rest soaks into the ground. Trickling down through the soil, the water reaches a level where it fills all the space between soil grains. This level is called the water table. Beneath it is the zone of saturation.

Ground water seeps along, following the slope of the land and the underlying rock. Weathering of rock goes on wherever water and air touch its surfaces. If the rock is limestone, great masses may dissolve away.

Falling rain dissolves a little carbon dioxide from the air. In the ground, water picks up more of the gas from decaying plant matter. The carbon dioxide reacts with the water to form carbonic acid, so ground water is really a weak acid solution.

If you spill an acid such as vinegar on crushed limestone, it fizzes. A chemical action takes place, in the course of which the acid dissolves some of the calcium carbonate of the stone. The same sort of action takes place, though more slowly, when ground water meets limestone. Seeping into cracks, the water slowly dissolves the rock. Cracks become enlarged, and eventually may form caverns like those at Luray, Virginia (opposite).

The cavern ceilings are festooned with *stalactites*. These grow as water drips from the ceiling and lime crystallizes from solution, forming rock again.

Photos: American Museum of Natural History (below); courtesy Luray Caverns, Virginia

MONUMENTS OF WEATHERING

Most ROCKS OF ARIZONA and southern Utah are sediments that were deposited long ago on the floors of inland seas. In time the earth's crust rose two miles above sea level, and the sediments formed a broad plateau. This weathered and was carved by the action of swift-flowing streams. One of the excavations, Bryce Canyon in Utah, is like a great, pink-walled theatre.

Rain continues to loosen the rock, and wind to blast it with flying sand. In some places, thin walls and slender towers are all that remain of the upper layers. As time passes, these too will disappear.

Photos: courtesy National Park Service (left); Union Pacific Railroad (above)

EROSION BY WIND

IN A DRY REGION, soils lie at the mercy of the wind. There is not enough moisture to make the grains stick together, nor enough plants to bind them. Wind sweeping over barren flats picks up the grains and whirls them away. Only gravel may be left behind.

The pictures on the left show a dust storm and its consequences. The wind can strip the valuable topsoil from plowed land, and bury other fields with drifts and dunes.

Sand gives the gales a million sharp tools. The grains cut into rocks and carve them into strange shapes. Near the La Sal Mountains in Utah, driven sand has hollowed out alcoves in the cliffs. In the picture of Looking Glass Rock, above, the size of the alcove is shown by the two horses in the foreground. The light spot is a window worn through the farther wall.

These are samples of erosion—the removal of earth materials, whether rock or soil.

Photos: courtesy U.S. Department of Agriculture (opposite); U.S. Geological Survey (above)

DEPOSITION BY WIND

WHAT THE WIND TAKES AWAY from one place, it gives to another. Fine dust may be carried hundreds of miles, until it is trapped by mountains or is dropped into the sea. But heavy sand grains just roll or hop short distances with each gust. Where the wind strikes an obstacle like a boulder or a clump of brush, it is checked, and the grains come to rest, forming a heap. This further slows the wind. Sand piles up as a dune.

From its birth, the dune is a moving thing. On the slope facing the wind, grains roll up to the crest, then tumble down the other side. In this way sand continually transfers from the windward to the lee side, so the whole dune creeps down-wind. If it encounters trees or houses, the dune may overrun them.

The dunes above are in Colorado; those in the picture on the right are in Death Valley, California.

Photos: Joseph Muench (right); courtesy Colorado State Highway Department (above)

EROSION BY WAVES AND CURRENTS

Winds agitate the ocean surface, driving currents and shaping waves. The waves surge endlessly, one after another. As each wave approaches shore, its lower part drags on the bottom. The crest outruns the rest of it, then plunges as a foaming breaker.

In the picture above, a headland juts out into the sea, where it receives the brunt of every storm. Wave-tossed boulders churn against the base of the cliff. The rock is eroded, the hill above is undermined, and great chunks collapse into the surf. Waves grind the material up, and currents carry it away. The work of erosion goes on and on; the headland wears back; the sea gains at the expense of the shore.

Photos: Free Lance Photographers' Guild

DEPOSITION BY WAVES AND CURRENTS

WHILE HEADLANDS RETREAT, other parts of the shore are extended by the forming of beaches, spits, and bars. Longshore currents do most of the work. Such a current, set into motion by waves striking the shore obliquely, sweeps along sand and other rock waste. Where the current enters the quiet water of a bay, its burden is dropped. If the bay is small, waves may toss the sediment inshore as a beach. If the bay is large, the sediment will be thrown across it as a bar (a long island parallel to the shore) or a spit (a long peninsula parallel to the shore).

In the view on the left, of Wrightsville Beach, North Carolina, the bottom is clearly seen through the shallow water around the margin of the beach. Here the waves break, flinging sand inshore. Wave and current action built the beach, as well as the tidal flats behind it.

In the picture below, a bar with houses and roads lies beyond the inlet. In the foreground, sand at the bottom of the inlet is continually shifted around by tides and currents. Some of it is bound to reach quiet water, where it will come to rest and form new shore features.

Photos: Fairchild Aerial Surveys

EROSION BY STREAMS

THESE PICTURES show a part of the plateau region of Utah, and the work of rivers in cutting it down. In the aerial shot above, the flat tops of the buttes in the distance are all on one level. This is the old surface of the plateau. In the course of time the rocks weathered; rivers carried away the fragments; valleys deepened.

In the picture on the left we see a branch of the Virgin River, one of the streams that has been carving the plateau. The slopes above it are made of rubble weathered from the cliffs. Some of the rubble slides all the way down to the river.

The river picks up sand and silt and rushes them downstream. At flood, it rolls large boulders along. Bashing one another, they knock off their edges and become rounded. They also gouge and deepen the stream bed.

With rivers eroding every valley, the plateau has been carved into a maze of deep gorges and narrow buttes.

Photos: Ewing Galloway; Fairchild Aerial Surveys

CANYON SCULPTURE

A RIVER HIGH IN THE PLATEAU COUNTRY flows down a steep gradient, or slope. The current therefore is swift and strong, and can transport a heavy load of fragments. At flood the river becomes mighty enough to dislodge chunks of rock and shove them along its bed. They gouge the bottom, making it deeper and deeper.

In a region where gradients are less, a stream erodes its bed slowly. Meanwhile the valley sides wear down, so that the valley becomes wide and shallow. In the plateau region, however, widening of the valleys has not kept pace with their deepening. Many a river has cut straight down through the rock, making a steep-walled canyon. Such is Zion Canyon in Zion National Park, Utah. The picture shows a section called the Narrows, where the Virgin River flows between sandstone cliffs 1800 feet high. In fair weather it is safe to ride along the river bottom, but the park rangers warn visitors to stay out of the canyon when a storm threatens. After one of the infrequent but hard rains that come in this region, a flash flood may roar down the canyon, filling it from wall to wall to a depth of 25 feet.

In the course of its history a river tends to "reach grade." This means that it cuts down toward a level where the gradient will be so slight that the stream slackens, depositing as much or more material than it erodes. At times in the past, the plateau rivers nearly did reach grade. Then internal forces of the earth heaved the plateau region upward. With gradients increased again, rivers speeded up and resumed cutting their channels. The sculpture of the plateau continued, and the canyons deepened.

Photo: courtesy Union Pacific Railroad

THE GRAND CANYON

PERHAPS THE FIRST DISCOVERERS of the Grand Canyon were Indians who settled near it a few thousand years ago. Later, Spanish explorers reached the Canyon while seeking fabled cities of gold. After the Civil War, explorers of another kind came to the plateaus and the Canyon. They were geologists, and one of their purposes was to learn the history of the region.

Major John Wesley Powell, who had lost his right arm in battle, led an expedition by boat down the Colorado. It was a dangerous undertaking. Often the party of nine men heard a warning roar of rapids ahead, and tied the boats while scouts went ahead on foot to reconnoiter. Sometimes they found the river foaming over great, jagged rocks. In such a case the party had to unload the boats and ease them down over the rapids by line, one at a time. After tying up below the rapids, they returned for the supplies, which they pack-carried along the narrow margin of shore.

At some rapids, the river poured through a passage that was just a slot between the rock walls. Since there was no foothold the party had to trust to the boats. A few times they capsized while shooting rapids, and barely managed to drag themselves out of the angry river. When their food supplies became soaked, it was necessary to stop and spread them out to dry.

Now and then the expedition halted briefly while Powell climbed to one of the terraces above the Canyon. From such a lookout he surveyed the great chasm, about a mile deep and from seven to fifteen miles wide at the top. A descending series of cliffs and benches made a vast stairway. The cliffs were mainly red sandstone, light gray limestone, and darker shale. Powell saw that they were edges of layers. Those on one side of the Canyon matched layers on the opposite side. This showed that the beds once had stretched unbroken across the space of the Canyon, and that the river had cut down through them and removed that great mass of material.

Photo: courtesy Union Pacific Railroad

NIAGARA FALLS

THE WATER PLUNGING OVER NIAGARA drops at a constantly increasing speed. It falls about 20 miles an hour after one second, and at more than 50 miles an hour after a drop of 150 feet. Beneath the Falls, the pounding water dislodges chunks of rock from the river bed. Swirling boulders dig a plunge pool and gouge into the cliff. The rock along the lip of the cliff is undercut, sticking out as a ledge. Finally the weakened ledge gives way and crashes down into the pool. This process goes on and on, wearing back the cliff and causing the Falls to retreat upstream. At the same time, the gorge below the Falls is lengthened.

The rock structure along the course of the Niagara River favored the development of a waterfall. Where shale was exposed, the surface wore down faster; where it was covered by dolomite, a much harder rock, the surface weathered more slowly and remained higher, forming a cliff over which the river poured.

The Falls have been surveyed from time to time, and the record shows that they have been retreating upstream at a rate of about five feet a year. The gorge below the Falls is seven miles long. If the Falls retreated that whole distance at the present rate, the retreat would have taken 7,392 years. But the river formerly carried less water than now, so geologists think the cutting of the gorge may have taken 25,000 years.

The picture shows a geologist lowered in a bucket beneath the lip of the Falls, at a point where it is deeply undercut. He is studying the rock to see if the observation platform above it has become endangered.

A few hundred yards upstream, the cap rock thins out, and the softer shale is exposed. If the Falls keep on retreating at the present rate, they will reach the soft rock in a thousand years. Then the river will erode its bed so swiftly that the Falls will disappear and be replaced by a stretch of rapids.

Photo: courtesy Ontario Hydro

ALLUVIAL FANS

WHERE A RIVER SLOWS DOWN, it loses carrying power and deposits sand in a series of bars. These may clog the channel, forcing the stream to overflow and cut a new course. Spreading its burden in one place after another, the river constructs a broad valley floor, or flood-plain.

In the desert region of California and Nevada, the land is broken up into mountain blocks separated by basins. Streams flow from the mountains into the basins, where the water evaporates without ever reaching the sea. Death Valley—really not a valley at all—is one of these basins. The picture shows where Furnace Creek and other streams enter it from the Black Mountains. The ranch at the lower right is irrigated with water from the creek. Notice the fan-shaped deposits below the creek and other streams. This type of structure is called an *alluvial fan* because it is made of *alluvium,* or river-laid material.

The creek rushes down the mountain slope, then is checked abruptly as it reaches the fan and the level floor of the basin. Its load of gravel and sand is deposited in the channel, quickly choking it and forcing the stream to take another course. After building up one part of the fan, the stream shifts to a part that is lower and builds that up. In this way the fan grows, always keeping its shape. In time the mountains will wear down and the fans will merge to form a broad plain.

Photo: Spence Air Photos

52

MATURE VALLEYS

A CANYON LIKE ZION (page 47) is bound to change. The river will cut deeper; its gradient will become less; it will slow down and stop cutting its bed; the canyon walls will wear back; in the end the canyon will be replaced by a wide valley with sloping sides.

Since a canyon has all these stages to go through, it is called a young valley. When a geologist describes a valley as young, mature, or old, he does not mean how many thousand years the valley has existed. He is considering how much work the stream has already done, and how much work remains before the valley will become wide and gently sloping.

All the rivers of a region go through a similar history. As they mature, the region matures. Highlands between the rivers are worn down to gently sloping hills and ridges.

The valley of the Delaware, which separates New York, New Jersey, and Pennsylvania, is part of a mature region (right). The rounded, low ridges are the edges of ancient mountain folds. Long ago, weathering and erosion wore the mountains down. Sediments eroded from them were spread over the area. Then rivers carved valleys through the sediments. The Delaware, in deepening its bed, cut right through the top of one of the buried ridges. Now the ridge has been exposed by erosion, and the Delaware courses through it, forming the Delaware Water Gap.

Photos: Ewing Galloway; Fairchild Aerial Surveys

OLD RIVER VALLEYS

THE LOWER PART of a river, as it reaches grade, becomes too sluggish to carry its burden of silt and clay. Part is deposited; filling in the valley, it makes a broad flood-plain. The river ordinarily keeps to a channel, but at time of flood it may overflow the whole plain.

Because the flood-plain is nearly flat, the river loops or *meanders* back and forth across it. Water going around a bend flows more slowly and placidly on the inside of the curve, and faster and more turbulently on the outside. Therefore sediment is deposited along the inside edge, while material is eroded from the outside edge.

By this process a loop stretches farther and farther across the plain.

While flooding, the stream may cut a new, straighter course, leaving some of its meanders cut off. In the picture of the Rio Grande Valley below, the river flows in the distance, while some of its old loops lie in the foreground, cut off as ox-bow lakes.

By pouring sediment into the sea, a river may build up the offshore bottom until it becomes dry land. Thus the Mississippi Delta was built and extended into the Gulf of Mexico. The picture above shows part of the Delta, with New Orleans half enclosed by one of the river's loops. Deposition on the Gulf bottom has increased the land by thousands of square miles.

When we think of it, the leveling of a continent and the extension of its shores depends on a power quite distant from the earth. Moisture-laden winds are set into motion by the heating of the atmosphere.

The heat comes from the sun, so it is really the power of our daytime star that brings about the leveling of uplands and the construction of deltas.

Photos: Fairchild Aerial Surveys (above); courtesy Standard Oil Company (New Jersey)

VALLEYS MADE YOUNG AGAIN

THESE PICTURES show the work of rivers that have become rejuvenated. On the upper left is a stretch of the San Juan River, in the plateau country of Utah. The meanders were formed during a period of old age, when the stream looped back and forth across a flood-plain. Then the plateau was uplifted, as had happened many times before. The river quickened, resumed eroding its bed, and entrenched the meanders.

Rainbow Bridge, in Utah, also was made by a rejuvenated stream. The aerial shot explains what happened. Notice that the upper abutment of the bridge rests upon a terrace. This is part of an old flood-plain, along which the stream meandered. Then the land rose, the stream quickened, and the meanders were entrenched. One of them looped around the location of the bridge, where at that time there was just a wedge of rock jutting toward the center of the valley. In time the river wore through the base of the wedge; erosion and weathering enlarged the hole and made a bridge.

The stream reached grade. A flood-plain developed at the level of the lower abutment of the bridge. Then came another period of uplift, which caused the river to erode down to its present level, where it courses through newly entrenched meanders. This three-story valley is a product of repeated uplift and rejuvenation. How many more such cycles will the river go through?

Photos: Spence Air Photos; courtesy National Park Service

GLACIERS

Mountains in many parts of the world are draped with glaciers like these in the Alps. How do such ice streams form?

Snow drifts into basins around the summits. Above a certain height, part of each year's snowfall lasts through the summer. New layers pile on the old. Their pressure causes the deep snow to pack into grains. Deeper still, grains jam together and form ice crystals.

The weight of the mass squeezes its edges outward. An expanding edge reaches a slope, where gravity tends to pull it down. But since the ice is stuck against the irregular rock bed, it cannot slide as a whole. Instead, thin sheets of ice slip against other sheets, a little at a time. Crystals split, slip, and reform, then split and slip again. By making millions of little shifts, the ice slowly flows downslope.

Photos: courtesy Swiss National Travel Office

ICEFALLS

Where a glacier channel takes a sudden drop, the ice must bend in flowing over the drop. Deep in the glacier, pressure holds the ice together so that it bends without breaking. But near the surface the pressure is much less, and this makes the ice brittle. Before it bends very much, it splits open. Melting may widen the cracks into crevasses. Between them, ice is left standing as giant walls. These tilt, then break from their foundations. Blocks as big as houses are rafted down-glacier as an icefall.

If the slope of the channel becomes gentle again, the blocks gradually settle into the body of the glacier, leaving the surface smooth.

The picture on the right shows the blocky surface of Lemon Creek Glacier, near Juneau, Alaska. For several years, scientists have been studying glaciers in this region. They measure the thickness and temperature of the ice, and the rate of flow. They compare these figures year after year, and find out whether the amount of ice in a glacier is increasing, remaining the same, or decreasing. A glacier acts as a giant thermometer, shrinking if the climate turns warmer, and growing if it turns colder. In the picture on the left, a geologist is seen investigating Lemon Creek Glacier.

Photos: Edward La Chapelle, courtesy Office of Naval Research and American Geographical Society

GLACIER SNOUTS

A GLACIER MOVES SO MIGHTILY, it seems no force could stop it from plowing on and on. But along its course the monster meets an enemy—the warmth of the lowland. During spring and summer, in a temperate climate, the cover of snow melts away, and the ice is bared, gleaming like emerald in the sunlight.

Water gathers in pools on the glacier top. It spills through channels of gemlike green, and sooner or later plunges down a crevasse. The water drains through hidden passages in the glacier, finally reaching the rock bed beneath it. There it flows through tunnels melted in the ice.

The glacier reaches a level where ice melts as fast as it arrives from above. There the glacier ends. If the climate is steady and the supply of ice regular, the end or "snout" of the glacier stays at one place. If summers become warmer or the supply of ice becomes less, the snout will retreat. If summers become cooler or the flow of ice increases, the snout will advance.

Two hundred years ago most glaciers were gaining ground. They overran farms in Norway and other countries. But during the past hundred years the glaciers have been shrinking.

The picture shows the snout of the Athabaska Glacier, in the Canadian Rockies. Farther up, the glacier tumbles down two icefalls. Below them the surface becomes so smooth that visitors stroll upon it, and ride over it in snowmobiles.

Photo: courtesy Canadian National Railways

GLACIAL EROSION

WHILE A GLACIER makes its way down valley, the cliffs and crags above it are constantly weathering. Water seeps into cracks in the rock, freezes, and expands in turning to ice. Splinters pried loose by the force of expansion tumble down on the glacier. They form a dirty ridge, a *moraine*, running down the surface on each side. The dark stripes on the glaciers shown on pages 60 and 61 are moraines.

Some of the rubble drops through crevasses and works its way to the bottom of the glacier. Rock chunks are also plucked from the channel bed. They lock into the ice, and the glacier drives them along, gouging the channel like a great rasp.

The load of dirt, gravel, and boulders is carried toward the glacier snout. As the ice melts, a blanket of rubble is left on the surface. Eventually it drops to the ground, forming a *ground moraine*.

In the view of the Athabaska Glacier, ground moraines run alongside the ice and around the snout. This material is wastage of the mountains.

Photos: courtesy Geological Survey of Canada; Canadian Government Travel Bureau

ALASKAN GLACIERS

THE MOUNTAINS lying along the coast of Alaska act as snow traps. They stand in the way of winds from the Pacific, so that the air is forced to rise, becomes chilled, and yields its moisture as snow. Wherever there are basins, snow piles up and builds deep, wide snowfields, which feed the glaciers.

By the time the winds pass over the mountain crest they are pretty well dried. Therefore little snow falls in the interior. No great glaciers are found there, though the climate is colder than along the coast.

Most of the snow falls on the seaward slopes, and it is there that the great glaciers flow. Some are thirty or forty miles long, a few miles wide, and several hundred feet thick. Prospectors once trudged up these glaciers in order to get to the gold-fields of the Yukon Valley, behind the mountains.

The Susitna Glacier, shown here, receives its ice from many snowfields. Streams descending from them pour into the trunk glacier. The twisting moraines show the pattern of flow. Snow covers the ice of the upper tributaries even in summer, but melts from lower reaches of the glacier. A good deal of ice melts, too. But where it is covered by moraines, there is less melting, and the moraines are left standing as ridges.

Photo: Bradford Washburn

GLACIAL SCULPTURE

As a glacier plows along, its stony "teeth" dig into the rock beneath it. Sometimes long grooves or other markings can be seen in bedrock over which a glacier has flowed. The upper picture on the next page shows how bedrock in the Chicago region was grooved by a glacier that plowed over it several thousand years ago. The lower picture shows rock on an island off the Labrador coast. A glacier rounded and furrowed it. The squarish holes are places from which the ice plucked chunks of rock.

Nunatak Glacier in Alaska (above) quarried the rock of its channel for thousands of years, until it hollowed out a wide trough running from the mountains to the sea. Then the climate turned warmer, and the glacier retreated. Ocean water filled the lower part of the trough. This is now a fiord—an arm of the sea cutting between rocky cliffs.

Photos: Bradford Washburn (above); Chicago Natural History Museum

U-SHAPED VALLEYS

PEYTO VALLEY in the Canadian Rockies (above) has the shape of a broad U, showing it was carved by a glacier.

River-cut valleys are much narrower. A stream flows so swiftly that it can be narrow and still drain the mountains. As the bed deepens, the valley becomes V-shaped.

Ice, on the contrary, flows so slowly that a great amount must be moving in order to drain the mountains. A glacier fills its valley from side to side. It carves the whole floor, deepening the valley in the form of a U.

A trunk glacier usually cuts deeper than its tributaries. The difference is revealed in places where glaciers have melted away. Tributary valleys often are left hanging above the main valley floor. The picture on the right shows a hanging valley in the Canadian Rockies, with a stream leaping from its cut-off channel to form a waterfall.

Photos: courtesy Canadian Government Travel Bureau

CIRQUES AND HORNS

A GLACIER usually starts from a basin high in the mountains. The picture above shows such a basin, or *cirque,* in the Canadian Rockies. The glacier once poured down through the part of the valley where the stream now flows.

Cirques are excavated by glaciers. Often a deep crack may be seen between the ice and the cirque wall behind it. Water drips down against the base of the wall, freezes in cracks in the rock, and pries off splinters. Sometimes the glacier is frozen against the rock, then lurches away, ripping out loosened blocks. These fall to the bottom of the glacier, which shoves them over the cirque floor. As the cirque deepens, its headwall becomes a towering cliff.

Glaciers sometimes lie on opposite sides of a ridge and quarry through it, cutting it into peaks. Such a peak may have cirques and glaciers on all sides. As the cirques deepen, the peak is left in the form of a "horn," like the Matterhorn in the Alps.

Photos: courtesy Canadian National Railways (above); Swiss National Travel Office

GLACIAL LAKES

FROM THE SNOUT of a glacier, a river of melt-water flows. Along its course are glacial lakes such as Lake Magog in the picture, which lies below Mount Assiniboine in the Canadian Rockies.

Lakes form in places prepared by the glacier. Perhaps a stretch of the valley floor was made of rock having so many cracks that the glacier plucked out pieces easily, and in this way excavated a basin for a future lake.

A lake may also be impounded by a natural dam. As the glacier pauses in its retreat, melting for quite a while at one place, rubble dropping there builds a moraine ridge across the valley. When the glacier resumes its retreat, the ridge is left behind and serves as a dam, holding back the meltwater and forming a lake.

Such a lake has a very short life. The glacial stream flowing into it carries a freight of rock scourings—sand, silt, and clay. The sand, being heavy, drops around the inlet, building a delta that rapidly extends into the lake. The clay particles float a long while, but in the end settle over the lake floor, gradually building it up and making the lake shallower. Meanwhile, at the foot of the lake, the outlet stream is cutting a notch in the moraine. Soon the dam is breached. As the lake drains, its floor is left dry, except for a stream of meltwater threading across the clay.

Photo: courtesy Canadian Government Travel Bureau

SIGNS OF A GREAT DISASTER

WE LIVE in a dramatic period of the earth's history. Lands are more elevated now than they have been at most times; mountain systems are vast and high, and are still rising. These conditions have upset equable climates of the past. Deserts have spread in regions where there were once continental seas, moderating extremes of temperature. Some lands have become unusually hot, while others have become unusually cold.

About a million and a half years ago, such factors, and others unknown, caused the climate of the whole world to turn colder—just by a few degrees, but it was enough to start ice accumulating on mountain heights. Glaciers grew and lengthened. In Greenland, Antarctica, and northern parts of Europe, Asia, and North America, ice floods poured down the mountain slopes, merging into great sheets that spread over the plains.

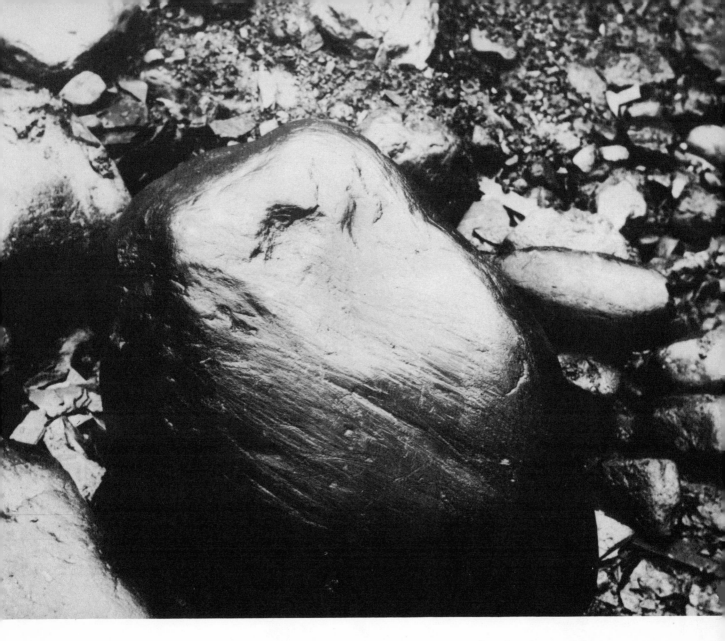

The paths of the ice sheets are traced from the same kinds of signs that glaciers leave behind them today. In many areas, bedrock has been scoured by the grinding passage of the ice. Moraine ridges of clay, gravel, and boulders lie where they were deposited around melting ice fronts; when these retreated, rubble was strewn behind them.

The picture on the left, from Illinois, shows a cut through a moraine, which was left by an ice front that stretched across the state. The picture on the right shows a boulder from a Pennsylvania moraine. Scratches and grooves were scored in it when the advancing ice shoved it over bedrock. Such boulders and moraines tell of a vast icy mantle, whose front of blue cliffs once spanned the continent from coast to coast.

Photos: Chicago Natural History Museum; U. S. Geological Survey

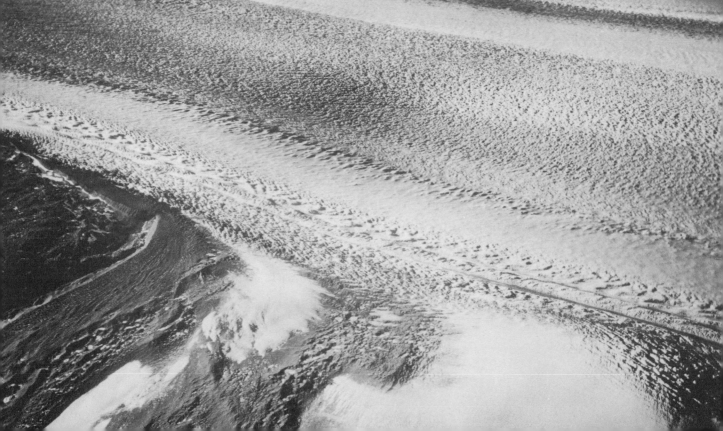

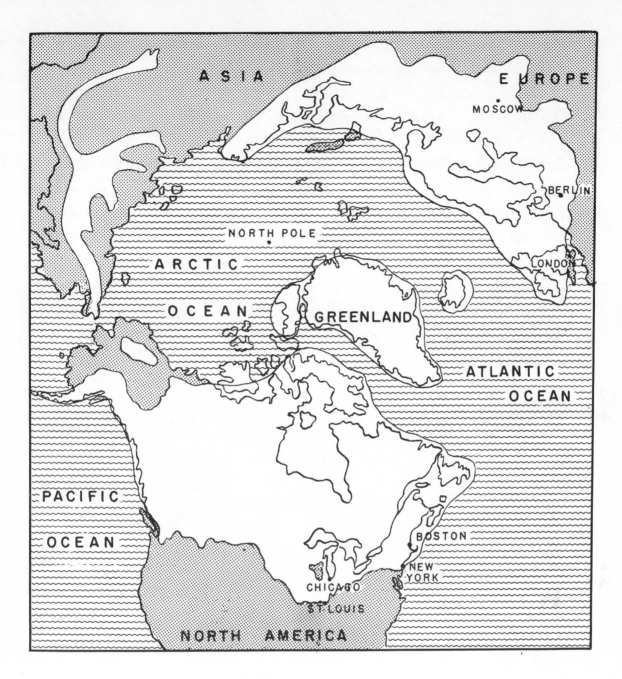

THE ICE AGE

SEVERAL TIMES during the last million years, ice sheets spread over northern Europe, Asia, and North America. Borings have been made through glacial rubble, and layers of four different ages have been found lying one on top of another. Sandwiched between them are old soils with remains of plants, showing that warm periods separated the four interludes of cold. In Greenland and Antarctica, ice sheets probably lasted all through the million years, which gives us reason to call that whole period, including the present, "the Ice Age." A glacier of the Antarctic continent is shown in the lower picture on page 80.

The map outlines the greatest extent of ice sheets in northern lands. Outlying parts of a glaciated region, such as the plains of southern Canada and the northern states, are blanketed with vast deposits of ice-borne material. But in areas of central Canada like the one shown in the upper picture on page 80, the bedrock lies stark and bare. An expanding mass of ice plowed over it, removing soil and shaving down the rock itself. Where mountains stood in the way, the ice streamed around them and through the passes, until only the peaks rose above the flood, like islands in a white sea. Finally the peaks, too, were overridden.

Will all this happen again? Will the sites of New York, Chicago, Boston, Berlin, and Moscow again be overwhelmed? No one can say whether the present warm period will be long-lasting, or whether, after a few thousand years, it will close as others have, to be followed by new floods of ice.

Photos: courtesy Royal Canadian Air Force; United States Navy Map: from
The Story of the Ice Age, *by Rose Wyler and Gerald Ames, reproduced by permission of the artist, Thomas W. Voter, and Harper and Brothers*

Part Two ∾ ∾ ∾

BUILDING
AND
REBUILDING

BUILDING AND REBUILDING

Rock weathers; mountains wear down; valleys age; sediments are carried from uplands and spread over the floors of seas. For thousands of millions of years the continents have been wasting away, yet they still rise above the level of the ocean. How can this be?

Land masses continue to exist because internal forces of the earth have repeatedly thrust them upward. Often the labors of rebuilding are accompanied by earthquakes and volcanic eruptions. In the pictures that follow, we see some effects of the colossal forces that reconstruct the surface of our planet.

Photo: Ewing Galloway

BIRTH OF A VOLCANO

ON THE 20TH OF FEBRUARY, 1943, all was peace and quiet around the town of Parícutin, in southwestern Mexico. Slight earth tremors had been felt, but nobody paid much attention to them. The farmer Dionisio Pulido was plowing his field when he noticed a puff of vapor coming from a hole in the ground. He rolled a stone over the hole and went on plowing. Then clouds began to rise out of the field. Pulido, frightened now, ran to town to report the event.

Two days later, as shown in the picture on the left, a volcano stood where Dionisio Pulido's field had been. Every few seconds there was a roaring explosion. Clouds billowed from the volcano's mouth. "Bombs" pelted down. Dust blanketed the countryside. In a few months, showering fragments had built up a cone 1,000 feet high (above).

Photos: Three Lions

87

MAGMA AND LAVA

VOLCANOES are powered by heat accumulated in the earth's crust. Many rocks contain traces of uranium and other elements that slowly decay and release atomic energy in the form of heat. After millions of years, rock may become so hot that it melts, turning into a doughy mass, or *magma*. Water vapor and other gases dissolve in the magma just as carbon dioxide dissolves in soda water.

When a bottle of soda water is capped, the carbon dioxide is held in by pressure. But remove the cap and the gas bubbles out. If the bottle is warmed and shaken, then opened, the carbon dioxide bursts out so fast that it carries the water along in a shower of foam.

The gases in a magma are "bottled up" by the overlying rock. If the cover has cracks and weaknesses, hot vapors will seep through them, melting the rock and opening vents. Gases blow off at the surface. This lowers pressure in the deep magma, allowing gases to continue bubbling from solution. A mass of hot foam shoves against the covering rock. If it breaks through, an eruption is started.

The boiling gases drive a stream of magma upward. As it erupts, vapors blow off. The magma quiets down, becoming lava, which may ooze like a heavy syrup, or form chunks like a stiff paste. The hotter it is, the more readily it flows. Chemical make-up also affects its behavior. One mixture will be stiffer, at a given temperature, than another.

Lava often pours freely from a vent and spreads around it in sheets. The face of the lava in contact with the air cools, forming a tough film of glass. This is flexible while hot. It stretches with the oozing of the lava inside it. Finally movement stops, as the lava hardens in ropy or billowy shapes like those in the pictures.

Photos: courtesy Hawaii National Park

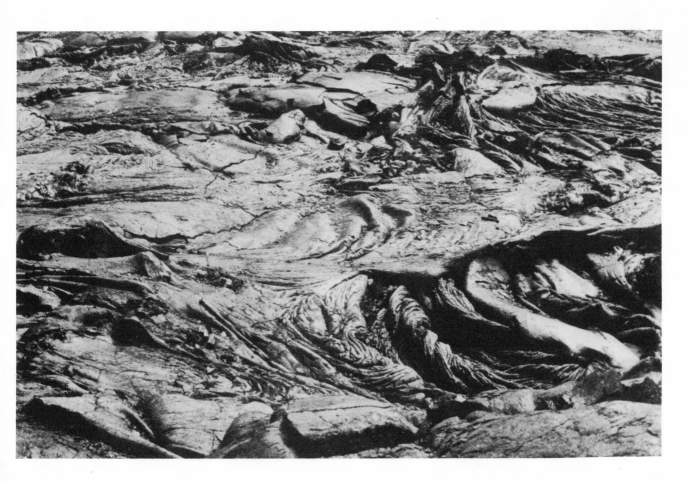

LAVA PRODUCTS

LAVA MAY DISPLAY a smooth, unbroken surface, but if we slice through it we find the inside as full of "holes" as Swiss cheese. The cavities in the specimen shown below were made by gases continuing to bubble out of solution as the material stiffened. When lava hardens quickly, there is little time for its substances to crystallize. They remain mixed, as they

were in the liquid, and as a result form a natural glass. If a sheet of manu-factured glass is struck with a hammer, a piece shaped like a shell will pop from the other side. If we hit a sheet of volcanic glass, the same thing happens. The shell-shaped fragment in the picture on the left was struck from volcanic glass.

Even after lava or volcanic glass has hardened, it contains water, which is chemically tied with other substances. Scientists have tested volcanic glass by heating. As the stuff softens, it bubbles and foams. The gas escaping from it is mostly steam.

When gobs of lava are blasted into the air during volcanic eruptions, they flash into foam. Much of this drops around the volcano as lumps of frothy glass, called pumice. The gas bubbles make it so light that it will float on water. Sometimes the froth takes the form of a "glass sponge" like that in the picture below.

As froth erupts, the bubble films harden while gases within them are still expanding. Millions of bubbles burst; their fragments form the dust that darkens the clouds of explosive eruptions. When splinters of volcanic dust are examined under a microscope, most of them prove to be curved, which shows that they came from ruptured bubbles.

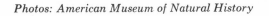

Photos: American Museum of Natural History

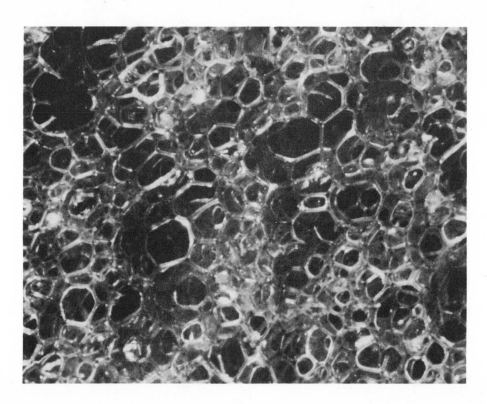

FLOODS OF ROCK

TWO DAYS after the birth of Parícutin volcano, a vent opened in a field about a quarter of a mile away. Lava spilled from it, flowing a few feet an hour. Six weeks later the stream was a mile long, half a mile wide, and a hundred feet thick. The surface cooled and hardened, forming a crust that hid the hot material inside. The crust was rafted along like ice on a river. Internal movement broke it into cakes shaped like floating ice pans. Glowing red lava showed through cracks between them. A mass of blocks jostled along the front of the stream, advancing as a moving wall. As blocks tumbled down the front, the wall rolled over them.

The picture on the left shows a flow of this kind streaming from a Japanese volcano. A sightseer who came for a close-up shot runs to get clear of the cascading lava.

Now and then, in various parts of the world, lava has flooded vast areas. The Columbia Plateau, which covers much of Oregon, Washington, and Idaho, was built by such deluges. Lava gushed from fissures, piling layer upon layer until old mountains and valleys were buried. Some outpourings in southern Idaho appear to be no more than a few centuries old. In the aerial view, showing an area round the Craters of the Moon, the lava flows look as though they spread there yesterday. On the nearest one, we can see how the crust fractured into rafts. Blocks cascading around the front made a pavement over which the stream rolled.

Photos: International News Photos; Spence Air Photos

CONES AND CRATERS

In a volcanic area, vents open here and there and erupt for short periods. Gases blasting from such a vent send up spurts of lava, much of which becomes frothy pumice. Showering down, it builds a cone-shaped heap around the vent. Eruptions through the top of the cone continually reopen the vent. A bowl-shaped crater is hollowed out by the blasts.

The aerial picture shows a typical cone and crater in the Mojave Desert in California. Sometimes erupting lava falls in clots big enough to remain hot and liquid, and they smear down the slope like icing on a cake.

Where eruptions have been on a large scale, as along the Cascade Range, cones have grown into mighty peaks like Rainier and Shasta. In the picture above, El Misti, a great volcano of the Andes, towers above the city of Arequipa, Peru.

All the great cone-shaped volcanoes of the world have been built by explosive eruptions of solids, alternating with flows of liquid lava. These usually break through some weak part of the upper cone. Then, streaming down the slope and hardening in sheets, they cement loose material and in this way strengthen the cone.

Photos: Spence Air Photos; courtesy Grace Line

VOLCANO-BURIED FORESTS

YELLOWSTONE PARK, in Wyoming, is located on a lava plateau. When volcanoes were erupting here ages ago, clouds of dust-laden vapor obscured the sky, and dust settled over the land like snow. Forests were shrouded with a gray mantle; some disappeared under drifts of dust and pumice.

Because the dust was fine, soil water readily dissolved many of its substances, among them silica. As water soaked into buried tree trunks, silica was deposited in mineral form in the tiny chambers of the wood. Then the walls of the chambers dissolved and their space was taken by quartz and other minerals, until finally the stumps were completely reproduced in stone. Now many of them are uncovered, standing as we see them in the picture on the right.

A different course of events produced the Petrified Forest of Arizona. About 160 million years ago this region was swampland such as that reconstructed in the scene below. Fallen tree trunks were buried under sediments containing volcanic dust, and in time became mineralized.

Photos: Joseph Muench (opposite); courtesy National Park Service; Ward's Natural Science Establishment

GEYSERS AND HOT SPRINGS

UNDER THE YELLOWSTONE REGION lies a magma, still hot and emitting gases. Ground water heated by the gases bubbles up in hot springs. Some of these erupt as geysers—fountains that turn on and off.

Most famous of the geysers is Old Faithful, so named because it gushes at more or less regular intervals, averaging 65 minutes. At first, water boils from the geyser mouth. Then steam and water shoot into the air. The main cause of this behavior is the shape of passages through which the steam and water rise. Some are like narrow tubes in the rock. Here and there they widen into chambers, which fill with ground water. The water in lower chambers is heated by steam coming up from the magma. A little of the hot water rises, but most of it stays below because it can't get through the narrow tubes fast enough.

Pressure below raises the water's boiling point, so it becomes superheated without boiling. Finally it gets hot enough to boil even under the high pressure. Bubbles of steam rise, expand, and push some water out of the geyser mouth. This lowers the pressure, which causes more superheated water to flash into steam. The steam roars up through the passages, blasting water into the air. When most of the steam has blown off, the eruption stops. The chambers begin to fill with water again, charging the geyser for another outburst.

Photo: courtesy Union Pacific Railroad

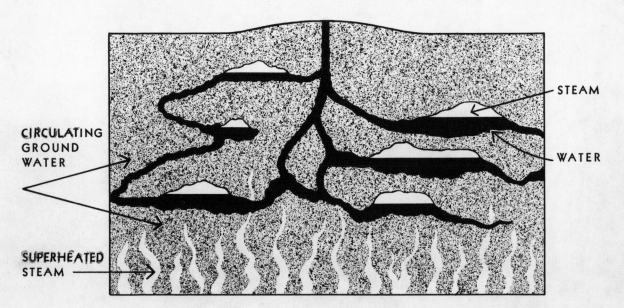

CIRCULATING GROUND WATER

STEAM

WATER

SUPERHEATED STEAM

VOLCANIC NECKS

WHEN A VOLCANO DIES, lava hardens in its throat as a plug of massive rock. The cone surrounding it, being composed mainly of loose material, crumbles and wears away. Meanwhile, the plug resists weathering. When the cone has dwindled to a formless hill, the plug remains standing like a monument. Devil's Tower, shown below, is a *volcanic neck,* marking a spot in Wyoming where a volcano, after its rage was spent, died and crumbled away.

The neck is made of the igneous rock called basalt. While the melt was cooling and shrinking, vertical joints formed. Later the joints were widened by weathering, and the rock between them was separated into flat-sided pillars.

In California, basalt lava has formed another pillared monument—Devil's Post Pile, shown in the picture opposite. Settlers must have thought the west a forbidding country, to name so many of its landmarks after the Devil.

Photos: Joseph Muench (opposite); courtesy National Park Service

EXPLOSIONS AND COLLAPSES

A VOLCANO may be undermined when explosions blast out the foundation of rock and magma supporting it. Such a climax is prepared by changes in the magma. Various substances are removed by crystallization; their loss causes the mixture to become stiff, and cooling makes it even stiffer. Gases are concentrated in the remaining liquid. As they strain to boil out, their pressure drives lava up the throat of the volcano. The lava squeezes out like toothpaste from a tube. Solid blocks of it pile up in the crater, building a dome that caps the volcano and holds in its gas pressure. This eventually becomes so great that it blows off the top of the cone. Vast clouds of vapor, dust, and pumice explode from the magma. Loss of all this material leaves a void beneath the volcano, and into it the hollow mountain collapses.

Crater Lake, in Oregon, marks the site of such a disaster. The nearly circular basin, five miles across and 2,000 feet deep, is a pit left by the collapse of a volcano. In its prime, it towered 12,000 feet high. Troughs radiating from the basin show that glaciers once streamed down the flanks of the mountain. During the eruption that destroyed it, about twelve cubic miles of material were lost. The magma gave its final gasp only a few centuries ago, creating the cone that now juts above the surface of the lake.

Photo: Spence Air Photos

VOLCANOES UNDER
THE SEA

MAGMAS DEVELOP under the sea as well as under land. Flows of lava pile on the ocean floor, building plateaus and volcanoes. For thousands of years such activity goes on unseen; then, somewhere on the sea's unbroken expanse, the water boils and releases clouds of steam. When a plane or ship passes that way, the spectacle is discovered. Through the steam, a dark mass of rock looms at a place where no land was ever charted.

The newborn island in the picture belongs to a group rising from the ocean floor 220 miles south of Tokyo, Japan. This rock is likely to disappear as suddenly as it popped up, for waves scatter the loose volcanic material, and collapses often cause it to sink beneath the surface. Yet building goes on; some day large islands may stand here.

All islands of the deep ocean are volcanic. The Hawaiians, for example, were built by vast lava flows. The main island is the top of a structure that covers nearly 4,000 square miles of the ocean floor. From its base to sea level is 15,000 feet, and from there to the top of Mauna Loa volcano is another 14,000 feet. If it stood on land, where we could see it all, this mass would be the most imposing mountain on earth. Lava from the Hawaiian vents is usually so fluid that it spreads out widely, building up the mountain in the form of a broad shield.

Photo: courtesy United States Navy

MOVEMENT OF THE EARTH'S CRUST

NOTHING IN NATURE is stronger than rock. It is not easily broken, we know, and under ordinary conditions it cannot be bent or squeezed out of shape. No wonder we think of the earth's rocky crust as rigid and un-yielding. This idea, however, is contradicted by evidence showing that in many regions the crust has been deformed on an enormous scale.

All mountain ranges testify to movements of the crust; peaks of the Canadian Rockies illustrate the story in a striking way. In the picture of Mount Robson shown here, a glacier streams down the giant's flank. Not long ago, other glaciers like it cut away the shoulders of the mountain, leaving its structure exposed. The rock is sedimentary. It lies in nearly horizontal layers. Shells of marine creatures are found in some of them, showing that at one time the sediments floored an open sea.

The layers are made up largely of shallow-water deposits, and their fossils are shallow-water creatures. Some series of layers in the mountains are several miles thick, yet shallow-water deposits occur at intervals all through them. This indicates that while the sediments were piling up, the depth of the water did not vary greatly—it always stayed pretty shallow. The only possible explanation of this seems to be that the floor of the sea was sinking while the deposits were accumulating. Sinking and deposition more or less balanced each other.

After the crust had sagged many thousand feet, its movement was reversed. The floor of the sea rose and became dry land. Some vast interior force of the earth buckled the crust upward until parts of it towered high above the plains to the east.

Photo: courtesy Canadian National Railways

ROCKS DEFORMED BY UPLIFT

As AN AREA RISES, it traps more rain and snow. Rivers are enlarged, and steep gradients quicken them and speed erosion. In time, underlying rocks are uncovered, revealing deformations caused by the uplift.

Sedimentary rocks are good recorders of such deformations. Since they are deposited in nearly horizontal layers, any later warping or tilting shows up clearly. Igneous rocks like granite, on the contrary, make poor indicators, since they are usually irregular masses.

Yet the very presence of granite at the surface tells something. It is a rock that forms at a considerable depth, and its exposure means that other rocks which formerly covered it have been removed by erosion. Granite

frequently makes up the bulk of mountain crests and cores. The Black Hills of South Dakota are granite (see page 20), showing that they lost a burden of covering rock during their upheaval. The presence of the granite suggests that the uplift was caused by the rise of a mass of granitic magma in the crust.

Surrounding the Black Hills are ridges formed by the broken edges of sedimentary beds. A similar *hogback* ridge, part of which is seen in the picture above, encircles the Zuni Uplift, in New Mexico. The picture on the left shows a ridge made of broken, tilted sediments ringing an area of uplift in Utah. In all three cases, the uplifted area had the shape of a dome, or would have had that shape, were it not cut down as it rose. The broken beds arch inward, pointing toward the summit of the eroded dome. Their slant shows how the rocks were deformed as movement of the earth's crust buckled them upward.

Photos: Spence Air Photos; courtesy U. S. Geological Survey

109

FOLDING

MOUNTAIN ROCK often is found crumpled into folds. The picture above shows folded layers in Glacier National Park, Montana. It seems amazing that the strong, brittle rock could have been kneaded like taffy. When this happened, it was not near the surface, we may be sure, for then it would have broken. During its deformation, the rock was buried deep beneath other deposits. The weight of the load above and around it created great internal pressure. This held the rock together while forces in the crust were squeezing it out of shape. Compression was so slow and steady that particles composing the rock could move slightly, then lock themselves in new alignments. Tiny shifts, multiplied billions of times, added up to a slow plastic flowing.

The Appalachian Mountain System was built by a combination of folding and general uplift. In the picture below, showing a section of the mountains in Virginia, long parallel ridges extend side by side. When the mountains were young, their surface forms may have followed the rise and fall of the folds, but erosion soon stripped away the tops. This left the edges of hard layers exposed.

Geologists have studied the structure of the mountains by comparing rocks of the ridges. In many cases, parts of the same beds, outcropping in neighboring ridges, curve upward toward each other. At one time they must have joined in an unbroken arch. Such an arching fold is called an *anticline;* a dipping fold is a *syncline.* Along the edges of the mountain belt, the folds are gentle and open, like waves. Toward the center, they are pressed close together, and some have become tilted or turned over on their sides.

Photos: Fairchild Aerial Surveys (below); courtesy U. S. Geological Survey

FAULTS AND FAULT MOUNTAINS

ROCK RESPONDS in a number of ways to stresses that pull and wrench through it. Being an elastic material, it will strain to a certain extent. This means it becomes deformed temporarily, in the manner of a steel spring, and will recover its old shape if the stresses diminish enough.

But suppose the stresses increase. At a certain point the rock yields by plastic flow, which produces permanent deformations like folds. If stress and strain become too great to be relieved in this way, the rock breaks.

In the picture on the left are sedimentary rocks with a fracture running across the beds. When we compare layers on opposite sides of the break, we see that they have shifted a few feet, so that those on the right are higher than corresponding layers on the left. The right side moved up or the left side down, or both moved in opposite directions. Whatever its direction or extent, movement along a plane of fracture is known as *faulting*.

In a region where upheaval of the crust is going on, some areas rise while others sink; or perhaps all rise, but unevenly. The conflicting movements fracture the crust, which becomes divided into great blocks. Along a fracture line, blocks on one side may rise while those on the other side sink or at least fail to rise so high.

In the picture on the right, the Tetons of Wyoming spring abruptly from the flat basin before them. The mountains and the basin meet along a fault line, where blocks on opposite sides have moved many thousands of feet in relation to each other. The uplifted block tilted as it rose, so that its top now forms a long westward slope, while its eastern edge towers as an escarpment.

Photos: courtesy U. S. Geological Survey;
Union Pacific Railroad

112

EARTHQUAKES

W$_{HEN}$ $_{ROCK}$ of the crust bends elastically, it stores the energy used in bending it. If it breaks, the parts rebound to their old shape, releasing the stored-up energy all at once with a mighty shock.

The view above shows part of the San Andreas Rift, a fault zone that spans California for 600 miles. Here it forms a pass cutting across the Temblor Range. The Rift developed because of rapid weathering of rocks broken by faulting. The greatest recorded disturbance caused the San

Francisco tragedy of April 18, 1906. The quake tumbled the buildings of the city, ruptured its water mains, and left it a prey to fire.

From surveys made after the quake, it was found that movement had taken place along 275 miles of the rift. There was practically no uplift or sinking; displacement was horizontal. Ground on the west side of the fault line had slipped toward the north; ground on the east side, toward the south. Roads and fences that crossed the fault were broken, many being carried out of line by 12 or 15 feet. The picture below shows one of the places where this happened. Areas of displaced surface extended four or five miles from the Rift on each side.

From recent surveys, it is known that straining along the Rift continues. On the west side, the crust has been pulling northward a little bit each year; and on the east, southward. If stresses and strains build up to the breaking point, rock along the zone of fracture will give way again, causing new quakes.

Photos: Spence Air Photos; Brown Brothers

RECORDING SEISMIC WAVES

IF A BASEBALL bat splits when you make a hit, your hands are stung by vibrations running through the wood. When rock splits and rebounds, the shock sends vibrations speeding through the earth. The rebound is the cause of the earthquake; the quivering *is* the quake. Near its source the crust vibrates so powerfully that houses and other structures may be shaken down. Farther away, the vibrations gradually lose force.

The vibrations are called waves (*seismic* or *earthquake* waves) because they travel by a form of wave motion. Similar vibrations will run through a steel bar if the end of it is struck with a hammer. The blow slightly compresses the steel at the bar's end. Being elastic, the steel rebounds to its old shape. In fact, it stretches past its rest position, giving a shove to the section of steel next to it; this section strikes the next, and so on. The stretching phase of the wave is called rarefaction. Each section of the bar keeps jumping from compression to rarefaction and back again, with diminishing force, until the vibrations die out.

In a compression-rarefaction wave, the material vibrates in the plane of the wave's progress. Another type of wave is set up if we hit the bar on the side. This wave also runs through the bar from end to end, but

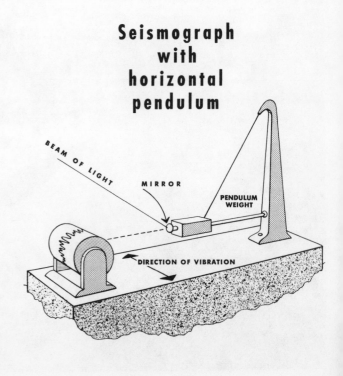

Seismograph with horizontal pendulum

BEAM OF LIGHT

MIRROR

PENDULUM WEIGHT

DIRECTION OF VIBRATION

the vibration is crosswise to the path of progress, like the "waves" made by shaking a bullwhip.

If we strike a steel ball instead of a bar, waves of each type radiate from the point of the blow. In the same way, seismic waves radiate through the earth.

The waves of an earthquake can be recorded at great distances. The recording instrument, the seismograph, is an adaptation of the pendulum, which is simply a suspended weight. The seismograph is mounted on bedrock in an underground vault. The pendulum weight hangs at rest, and tends to stay at rest even when the support beneath it—the earth's crust—moves. A change in relative position of the rock and the weight shows that the rock has moved.

If the weight were hung vertically, it would have to be suspended very high and the seismograph then would not be accurate. In the Milne-Shaw type of seismograph, shown in the picture on the left, the weight is suspended horizontally, like a gate from a gatepost. It is allowed to sag slightly below the horizontal, so that if it moves it will always return toward rest position.

Opposite the weight, a rotating drum is anchored in bedrock. When the rock vibrates, the drum shakes with it. Meanwhile the pendulum weight stays at or near rest position. In the arrangement shown in the diagram, a mirror is fixed on the weight. A beam of light, reflected from the mirror, falls on the drum, which is covered with photographic paper.

As the drum turns, a line is made on the paper. If the drum is not quivering, the line is straight. When it quivers, the line becomes wavy. This wavy line is a seismogram—the portrait of an earthquake.

The picture above shows pendulum apparatus in the seismographic vault of Columbia University. The recording is done photographically in a darkroom.

Photos: courtesy U. S. Coast and Geodetic Survey; Columbia University

UNDERSEA QUAKES AND TSUNAMIS

MORE EARTHQUAKES originate under the ocean than under the continents. This is not surprising, considering that nearly three-fourths of the surface of the planet is ocean-covered. Seismologists plot the points of origin of quakes on a map, and find that they cluster thickly along certain deep trenches in the Pacific floor.

These trenches—among them the Atacama Deep off the coast of Chile, the Japan Trench, and the Aleutian Trench off the Aleutian Island chain—are part of a great zone of unrest that rings the Pacific. It is believed that the bottom of the trenches are continuing to sag; this causes rock of the ocean floor to break and rebound, setting off earthquakes.

Occasionally, an undersea quake produces its own kind of disaster—a vast wave, or series of waves, known to scientists by its Japanese name, *tsunami*. On the open ocean, a tsunami may pass under a ship unnoticed, for it is only a foot or so high. The distance between two wave crests may be from 100 to 400 miles, which means that enormous volumes of water are involved in the wave motion. The advance of a wave is as swift as several hundred miles an hour. Harmless on the open ocean, it may pile a mountainous wall of water against a shore.

On April 1, 1946, a disturbance along the Aleutian Trench set off an earthquake and a tsunami. Apparently, rebound of a rock mass

gave a shove to the water above it. The shove passed to the surface, where a tsunami bulged up and pressed out on all sides.

The waves of this tsunami were studied at several places. They measured about 100 miles from crest to crest, yet passed a given point within 12 minutes of each other. The first one traveled from the Aleutian Trench to Honolulu, 2,240 miles away, in 4 hours and 34 minutes, making an average speed of 497 miles an hour.

A short while before the arrival of the tsunami at Hawaii, people noticed that the sound of the surf had died away. They looked and saw that the water had withdrawn far from the beach. It was a warning. Those acquainted with the ways of the tsunami knew that water was piling up at sea. A few minutes later a towering wave roared in and swept over the shore. The water withdrew again, and a second wave came, followed by several others. The picture shows the destruction they brought to one place, an Army air base on Oahu.

The United States Coast and Geodetic Survey keeps track of tsunamis in order to warn coastal areas of their approach. Several stations have a detector that automatically announces the passage of the waves. The diagram shows how it works. A length of six-inch pipe is set in the sea, open end down. As the ocean surface rises, air pressure in the pipe increases. This pushes mercury in a U-tube to a point where it closes an electric circuit, setting off an alarm.

Photos: courtesy U. S. Coast and Geodetic Survey

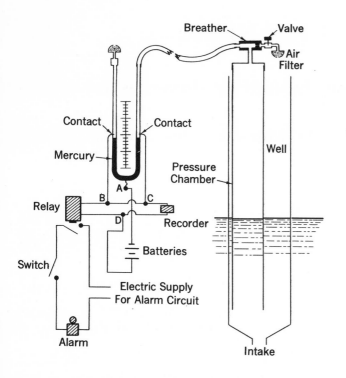

119

A RESTLESS PLANET

THIS MOUNTAIN and boat are symbols of some of our planet's unsolved mysteries. The peak is Chimborazo of Ecuador, a volcano capping the Andes. The ship is a research vessel of the Scripps Institution of Oceanography, at La Jolla, California. It is equipped to sound the deep Pacific trenches, one of which parallels the Andes.

The western mountain chains of the Americas, the Cordilleras, continue to rise, while ocean trenches near them continue to sink. Why? One factor is that the mountains are made of rocks lighter than those of the ocean basins. Scientists find that the force of gravity over the mountains is less, and that around the trenches greater, than the expected values. This indicates that the mountains are on lighter blocks of the crust, and the trenches on denser blocks. Deep down, we suppose, all blocks "float" in a layer of material that can yield plastically to forces operating over a long period. According to the theory of *isostasy*, or "equal standing," lighter blocks tend to rise and heavier ones to sink, so that all approach levels at which their values of gravity will be equalized.

In some places, the earth seems to be defying this principle. Gravity values right over the Java Trough are less than expected, suggesting that the sea floor ought to be rising instead of sinking. What is pulling it down? Convection currents in the crust, according to one theory. Supposedly, differences of temperature within the earth set up very slow currents, causing some masses of material to rise while others sink.

The theory of convection currents runs into one big difficulty. The great zones of rising and sinking, like the one marked by the Cordilleras and the Pacific trenches, are very long and narrow. It is hard to imagine that they could be caused by vertical currents. Many scientists therefore favor an older idea, according to which a layer of material in the earth is contracting as it cools. Layers above it are forced to shrink. They do this by folding, and by breaking and partly sliding over one another. The fracturing produces earthquakes; magmas erupting through the breaks create volcanoes.

Photos: courtesy Grace Line; Scripps Institution of Oceanography

CREATION OF THE EARTH

THE EARTH and the other planets of the sun's family are arranged nearly on one plane, and all circle in the same direction. A well-ordered family, indeed! We marvel at the system, and try to imagine how it came to be. A theory was proposed two hundred years ago by the philosopher Immanuel Kant, and was later developed by the mathematician Laplace. According to this theory, the material of the solar system once existed in the form of a huge, flat cloud of gas, slowly rotating. Matter was pulled by gravitation toward the center, where the sun formed. As the cloud shrank, it spun faster, and outer portions were flung off as streamers or rings. These condensed and formed the planets.

In the last fifty years, scientists have discovered that the earth has a composition differing greatly from that of the sun. By means of the spectroscope, most elements known here have been detected in the atmosphere of the sun and other stars; and some have been identified in the thin clouds of dust and vapor that are strewn through space. From such findings, scientists have been able to estimate "cosmic abundances" of the elements—their relative amounts throughout the universe. When cosmic abundances are compared with abundances on the earth, a striking difference appears. Whereas the universe is made up largely of hydrogen and helium, the earth has only traces of these two gases. The same is true, apparently, of Mercury, Venus, and Mars, the planets nearest the earth and comparable to it in size.

Here is a riddle! What happened to supplies of hydrogen and helium that these planets must have had originally?

Other gaseous elements also are scarce on the terrestrial planets (the earth and the other three). This suggests that the planets were formed by the gathering of solid particles rather than gases. Dust collected into lumps, the lumps into large masses, and the masses into worlds. While all this was happening, gases drifted away.

Small quantities of gases, however, were trapped in the lumps of matter. Some condensed into liquids; among these was water, which helped to paste the lumps together as gobs of mud, slush, or ice.

When the planet Earth was formed, it possessed neither atmosphere nor ocean. But within its solid material was a store of water vapor and other gases. As time went on, heat was produced by the decay of radioactive elements. Magmas formed. Volcanoes poured out deluges of lava and clouds of vapor. The escaping gases began to make an atmosphere. Steam condensed; cloudbursts pelted down. Water poured into the great hollows of the surface, where the ocean formed and grew.

Such is the picture we draw of our planet's early days. But the picture will develop and change as scientists go on uncovering secrets of the universe.

Drawing by Gerhard Ramberg

Part Three ∾ ∾ ∾

THE
PARADE
OF LIFE

THE PARADE OF LIFE

AMONG THE PLANETS of the solar system, only the earth has conditions fit for living things. Mercury and Venus, which circle near the sun, become too hot. Mars and the outer planets, located farther away, are too cold. Plants and animals require temperatures at which water stays liquid, for their body fluids are water containing dissolved substances.

The size of a world is important. Little Mercury has a gravity so weak that it cannot hold an atmosphere. The giant planets, with their powerful gravity, retain a blanket of poisonous gases. The earth's gravity is just strong enough to hold a mixture of gases suitable for life.

For hundreds of millions of years, our planet has been inhabited by living creatures. Many have left recognizable traces in the rocks. These traces, or fossils, enable us to review a wonderful parade of life. The following pictures show a number of fossils, and also paintings of the creatures as they may have looked when alive.

Photo: Chicago Natural History Museum

FOSSILS

MILLIONS OF YEARS AGO, the sea floor off the west coast of South America was uplifted and became dry land. In time the land was eroded, exposing an ancient sea bottom hardened to rock. In it we find shells of marine creatures, some of which are shown in these pictures.

Usually, the soft tissues of animals and plants were eaten or quickly decayed. Only shells, bones, or other hard parts lasted long enough to become fossilized.

Fossils are found only in sedimentary rocks. There are none in igneous rocks, whose heat would have destroyed any plant and animal remains.

Photos: courtesy Standard Oil Company (New Jersey)

ANCIENT SEA DWELLERS

In 1910 a geologist, while exploring outcrops of shale in British Columbia, discovered a remarkable bed of fossils. The Burgess Shale, as it is called, formed on the sea bottom from ooze that contained a great deal of plant and animal matter. Carbon left from this organic material gives the shale a dark color.

In some hollow of the ancient sea floor, the rotting of dead plants and animals used up all oxygen from the water and replaced it with poisonous gases. Animals that drifted into the stagnant hollow were suffocated, and their corpses sank into the ooze. Because of the lack of oxygen, no living creatures were

there to eat them, and their flesh did not decay. Sediments settled over the remains and buried them.

As layers of ooze piled up over the bodies, their substances slowly dissolved and were carried away. Only the carbon remained; it was pressed into black films that became almost perfect prints of the bodies. In this way, even fragile creatures like jellyfishes were fossilized. When the shale is split into sheets, prints lying between them are revealed.

The lower picture on the next page shows two fossils from the Burgess Shale, preserved as carbon films. They represent animals

130

called trilobites, which means "three-lobed." The name refers to lobes or divisions of the shell formed by creases running down the back. The shell material was the same as that of modern crabs and lobsters, which are distant relatives of the trilobites. Most trilobite fossils show only the shell, but in these specimens even the legs and other delicate parts are reproduced.

The trilobites had a long history. They first appeared about 400 million years ago, and after ruling the sea bottom for 100 million years, all died out.

Limestone is another fossil-bearing rock. The upper picture shows a piece of limestone from Iowa enclosing a fossil crinoid, or "sea lily." When the crinoid died it was buried in a limey ooze. The water bathing it held a lot of lime (calcium carbonate) in solution. As substances of the crinoid's body dissolved, they were replaced with lime. Gradually the entire form of the creature was reproduced in this mineral.

In spite of its flower-like appearance, the crinoid was an animal. A flexible stem anchored it to the sea floor. Tentacles around its mouth resembled petals. Waving, they set up a current of water that carried food bits into the mouth.

Models of a crinoid, trilobites, and other animals are shown in the scene on the opposite page. The octopus-like creature with the coiled shell is a cephalopod or "head foot." It is attacking a trilobite.

Photos: courtesy New York State Museum; Ward's Natural Science Establishment; Smithsonian Institution

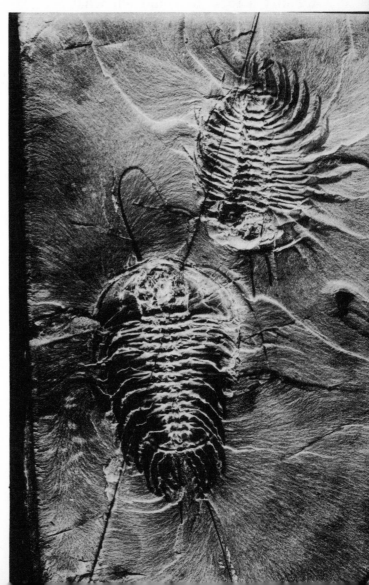

THE RECORD OF THE ROCKS

BEFORE 1800, scientists did not know the order in which the rocks had been formed, so they could not tell the order of fossils, nor understand the history of the earth. Then a key to the puzzle was discovered by William Smith, an Englishman who collected fossils as a hobby. Smith was a surveyor; he worked at planning canals and choosing locations for quarries. For these purposes he had to know what kinds of rock lay under the surface. He had learned that beds of several different rocks rested one upon another in the same order all over England. When he was able to identify a rock, he could tell what beds lay under it.

Because certain beds looked alike, Smith often found it hard to decide which one he was dealing with. Then he discovered that each rock layer held a set of fossils differing from those in other layers, so that the fossils could be used to identify the rocks.

After Smith's discovery, his guide fossils were found in various parts of Europe and Asia. This showed that the rocks containing them belonged to the same series of layers.

Most rocks of England and Europe were formed from marine sediments. In the past, as now, conditions in the sea were similar over great areas, and marine creatures could spread for thousands of miles. As a result, fossils of a given species now are found distributed across a continent, or even around the world.

In time, geologists found additional sets of fossils which they used to identify other rock series. Some of these come from the Grand Canyon, the most magnificent cross-section of rocks in the world.

In the aerial shot on the next page, the Canyon runs diagonally across the lower right-hand corner. A tributary, Bright Angel Creek, enters it from the middle ground. Notice that the upper rocks are layered, while the deepest rock is not. This is schist, made of very ancient sedimentary rocks transformed by pressure. Its structure tells of movements that folded the earth's crust and built mountains.

In time the mountains wore down. The sediments from their erosion were carried elsewhere, causing a break in the record at this place. Afterward the area sank and was covered by a sea. New sediments accumulated, becoming the layers of sandstone, limestone, and shale that lie above the schist. Several times, the area was uplifted and eroded, causing parts of the record to be lost. The blank pages can be filled in by our knowledge of sediments deposited in other places.

Step by step, geologists have established the order in which the sedimentary rocks of the world were deposited. As a result of their work, the rocks have become a book in which we read the story of the earth and its life.

Any story is easier to understand if it is divided into parts and chapters, so geologists

have divided the earth's story, choosing great episodes of mountain-building to mark the ends of parts, and lesser events to mark the ends of chapters. The parts are called eras, and the chapters, periods.

After the order of the rocks was established, scientists tried to estimate their ages. The best results are obtained by comparing their content of uranium with the quantities of its decay products. The breakdown of uranium goes on slowly and always at the same rate, so the amount of decay can be used as a measure of time. It tells how long decay of uranium has been going on in a rock—in other words, how old the rock is. This method is not used with sedimentary rocks because the uranium and decay products in them come from earlier rocks and tell nothing about the age of the sediments. Often, however, it is possible to obtain rough dates for sediments by finding out the age of igneous rocks sandwiched between them.

With the rocks dated more and more accurately, the table of eras and periods becomes a time scale of the earth's history. This time scale is shown on the next page.

Photo: Spence Air Photos

133

THE EARTH'S TIME SCALE

ERAS	PERIODS		ESTIMATED TIME OF BEGINNING (IN MILLIONS OF YEARS AGO)
CENOZOIC ("of recent life")	QUATERNARY	Recent	
		Pleistocene	2
	TERTIARY	Pliocene	10
		Miocene	30
		Oligocene	40
		Eocene	50
		Paleocene	60
MESOZOIC ("of middle life")	CRETACEOUS		130
	JURASSIC		168
	TRIASSIC		200
PALEOZOIC ("of ancient life")	PERMIAN		235
	CARBONIFEROUS		315
	DEVONIAN		350
	SILURIAN		375
	ORDOVICIAN		445
	CAMBRIAN		550
PROTEROZOIC ("of former life")	. . . .		1200
ARCHEOZOIC ("of beginning life")	. . . .		2000

GEOLOGISTS have summed up the record of the rocks in this time scale, which is read from the bottom upward, following the normal order of the rocks. The chart on the opposite page shows animal and plant forms typical of the succeeding periods. The parade of life seems to begin suddenly in the Cambrian period, about a half billion years ago. This is because Cambrian rocks are the oldest that contain good, clear fossils. But the creatures of the Cambrian were not the first living things. Many of them, such as trilobites, were quite complicated. They must have come from a long line of ancestors.

We know almost nothing about such ancestors. The rocks of their times have gone through so much compression and metamorphism that their fossils have been destroyed. Pre-Cambrian shales and slates contain carbon that must have come from living matter, but few fossils remain to tell us what the organisms were like. They probably were small, soft-bodied things that seldom became fossilized.

Photo: courtesy Bryn Mawr College

THE SEA WAS THEIR HOME

DURING CAMBRIAN TIMES, while mountains dominated both coasts of North America, the interior was gradually flooded. Sediments piled up on the sea floors, building pavements of rock between the highlands. These layers record the life of the Cambrian. They have yielded no trace of land plants or animals. The sea, so far as we know, was the home of all living things.

In the picture on the right, taken in northern New York, we see traces of microscopic plants that inhabited the sea floor. They grew in dense colonies. Each plant deposited a little lime, and altogether they built a film of this mineral. Then other generations of plants grew up and laid new films on top of the old, in this way constructing a dome. Ooze settled over some of the domes and turned to limestone. In time, the rock was exposed and eroded. The last ice sheet plowed over it, shaving down through some of the fossil domes. The surface of the rock, smoothly polished, shows how the domes were built up with larger and larger shells.

When the seas drained away, their floors became plains. Weather and rivers wore down the land, causing a break in the record which marks the division between the Cambrian and the next period, the Ordovician. From this period, too, no traces of land-dwelling life have been found. The continent was a wasteland of rock and rubble.

Around the margins of the sea, storm waves rolled in and cast strange burdens upon the shore. The picture on the left shows an Ordovician beach as it may have looked after a storm. Matted seaweed loops along the high-water line. Some trilobites and cephalopods lie stranded. One type of "head foot" is a nautiloid with a long, cone-shaped shell. This was divided by partitions forming numerous chambers. The animal occupied the outer one. As it grew, it built larger and larger chambers, closing off each old one with a wall. Sometimes a shell with its many unused chambers grew to be fifteen feet long. One line of nautiloids developed a coiled shell.

Photos: Painting by Charles R. Knight, Chicago Natural History Museum; courtesy New York State Museum

FROM SEA TO LAND

FOR A BILLION YEARS or more, the shore of the sea was a frontier that life could not cross. Then at last, during Silurian and Devonian times, some groups of living things became fit to live on land. Not on high, dry land, to be sure, but on flats bordering bays, lagoons, and estuaries.

Water plants clung to the bottoms, submerged when the tide was in and exposed when it was out. In time, their descendants developed coverings that prevented them from drying up while they lay exposed to the air.

The earliest land plants known from fossils grew in the form of leafless, branching stems. Part of the stem system lay underground, anchoring the plant. Among later types, leaves and roots developed. Swamps like those in the picture became overgrown with giant rushes and ferns.

The first animals to populate the swamps belonged to the tribe of arthropods, "the joint-footed." Creatures resembling crabs managed to stay out of water for a while, so long as their gills remained moist. Eventually, some lines developed tubes for breathing air; with these they could live entirely out of water. Among their descendants are today's insects, spiders, scorpions, centipedes, and millepedes.

During the first invasions of land, the only backboned animals, the fishes, remained in the sea. Their remote ancestor had been some worm-like creature with a rod of cartilage (gristle) running through the center of its body; the rod supported a central nerve cord. In the fishes, this rod developed into a spinal column made of movable vertebrae. Other bones were attached to them. This internal skeleton gave the fish a big advantage. It was light in weight, and it was flexible, allowing the fish to bend its body and whip through the water.

Fishes of the Devonian inhabited shallow bays and lagoons. These waters often were clogged with decaying vegetation, which used up oxygen and replaced it with poisonous gases. Yet the fishes did not suffocate. Having lungs in addition to gills, they were able to come to the surface and breathe air. One type had another useful structure, fins set on muscular lobes. When a lagoon dried up, the lobe-fin fish could wriggle toward the nearest remaining pool. The picture on the upper right shows lobe-fins as they may have appeared when crawling on land.

From fishes such as these came the early amphibians. A typical kind, Diplovertebron, is shown in the lower picture. The name amphibian means "leading a double life," in the sense that the amphibian begins its life in the water, then becomes able to exist on land.

The early amphibian was little more than a fish on legs. When stranded by the draining of a pool, it used its legs to crawl toward water, its true home. The amphibian's legs were not a means of conquering the land, but of escaping from it.

Photos: painting by Charles R. Knight, Chicago Natural History Museum; paintings by F. L. Jaques, American Museum of Natural History

THE EGG WITH A SHELL

MARSHES BORDERING the interior seas were well suited to amphibians. There they found plenty of water in which to live and breed. The amphibian's egg was like that of the fish—small and soft. It had to be laid in water so it wouldn't dry up. It held food material for the embryo (the young developing in the egg) but the supply was small. This meant that the young one had to hatch while it was still very tiny. It began life in the way a frog does today—as a tadpole breathing with gills. It lived in the water for quite a while before its lungs developed.

The amphibians thrived so long as the continent remained half flooded, with broad marshes surrounding the shores. But times changed. In the course of millions of years the land was uplifted here and there, and great swampy regions became dry. What were the amphibians to do? Many lines died out. Others changed in ways that made them better suited to the changing world.

Fossils of the animal pictured here were found near the town of Seymour, Texas, in whose honor the beast was named Seymouria. It is a puzzling creature, with a skeleton midway between the amphibian and reptilian forms. Ever since its discovery, paleontologists have debated whether it was a reptile or an amphibian. In any case, they consider it a link between the two groups.

The reptiles took a step forward by developing a large, shelled egg. It was laid on land, and the shell kept it from drying in the air. The large supply of food in the yolk enabled the young to stay in the egg longer than an amphibian does, and to develop further before hatching. From the moment it broke out of the shell, the young reptile was an air-breathing animal at home on land.

Photo: painting by F. L. Jaques, American Museum of Natural History

EARLY REPTILES

DURING THE PERMIAN PERIOD, the interior of North America gradually rose, and seas drained. As a result, some regions became drier, and suffered greater extremes of heat and cold. Swamps disappeared, leaving fewer places where amphibians could live. Their numbers decreased; many kinds died out.

Reptiles fared better, because they could become suited to the new conditions. Two lines developed a sail-like structure on their backs. Fossils of these creatures have been found from Pennsylvania to Texas. They lived along the borders of a hot desert region. Perhaps the "sail" was really a kind of radiator, serving to get rid of excess heat.

In the scene above, the artist presents a marsh like those that lined rivers and seas of North America during the Permian. A forest of tree ferns and

other swamp vegetation stands in the background. On the right is a clump of rushes, ancestors of the modern horsetails.

In the foreground, two kinds of sail-backs sprawl on a mud flat. The smaller type, with knobs along the spines of the sail, was a harmless plant-eater. The larger type had front teeth that were longer and sharper than the rest. These teeth, plainly made for tearing flesh, prove that the creature was a hunter and flesh-eater. It has been named Dimetrodon, which means "having teeth of two sizes."

Perhaps Dimetrodon preyed upon smaller, lizard-like reptiles such as those on the left-hand side of the picture. On the right is a little triangular-headed amphibian, which also may have been chased by Dimetrodon.

Photo: painting by Charles R. Knight, Chicago Natural History Museum

143

FROM CRAWLING TO RUNNING

IN PERMIAN TIMES, North America and other continents stood higher than they do today. Swiftly flowing rivers carried away much material, depositing it in places now covered by the ocean. In this way part of the rock record was lost. Later, when seas again invaded the land, new sediments were laid down on the eroded surface.

The break resulting from erosion is taken as a dividing line between the Paleozoic and Mesozoic eras. The Mesozoic, which lasted about 150 million years, was the great age of reptiles.

Early in the Triassic, the first period of the Mesozoic era, an interesting tribe of reptiles developed in South Africa. One of their members was the creature pictured here. It is called Cynognathus, meaning "Dog-jaw." The name refers to the fact that its skull and teeth resemble those of a modern mammal such as the dog.

In more typical reptiles, the teeth are all of about the same size and shape, but in Cynognathus they differed according to their use. In the cheek were molars for grinding; in front were incisors for nipping, and canines for tearing flesh.

Reptile means "creeper," but Cynognathus had advanced from creeping. Its legs did not sprawl out from its sides like those of amphibians and very early reptiles. Instead, they were placed beneath the body. In this position they raised Dog-jaw's belly off the ground, enabling it to walk or run. In time, lines of agile creatures built on this plan developed into mammals.

Photo: painting by F. L. Jaques, American Museum of Natural History

INVASION OF THE SEA

EARLY IN THE AGE of reptiles, certain lines gradually migrated back to the sea. Their ancestors no doubt inhabited shores and shallows, and pursued slow-moving amphibians. Succeeding generations became better and better adapted to life in the water. Their legs developed into flippers that made them rivals of the fishes, enabling them to chase the swiftest game.

One tribe, the plesiosaurs, had a body resembling a turtle's, from which extended a long, snake-like neck. The plesiosaur moved its head about freely, surveying the water. When it sighted a fish it would dart its head and strike the prey as a snake does.

Sometimes a plesiosaur fossil is found with a collection of rounded, polished stones lying where the stomach would have been. Evidently these

were swallowed from time to time, as among certain modern birds, and were carried in a gizzard that worked as a meat grinder. The stones were jounced around, helping to mash up chunks of food which the plesiosaur gulped down whole.

Long before the porpoise existed, the reptiles produced an equivalent, the streamlined ichthyosaur, or "fish-reptile." There were several kinds, varying in length from five to thirty feet. With a shark-like tail and fin-like flippers, the ichthyosaur sped through the water, overtaking fishes and squids.

Well-preserved ichthyosaur fossils have been found in shales of Holz-maden, Germany. Some female specimens carry the fossils of unborn young. This shows that the ichthyosaurs had become completely independent of land. Egg-layers no longer, they gave birth to living young in the water.

Photo: painting by Charles R. Knight, Chicago Natural History Museum

DINOSAUR HUNTERS

PALEONTOLOGISTS hunt the most fantastic of all game—dinosaurs. Some of these creatures were enormous. The picture below shows a dinosaur footprint big enough to serve as a bathtub.

Digging up the monsters' skeletons is hard work. Often their fossils are found in desert regions, where scientists toil for months to excavate a specimen or two.

Millions of years ago, while the skeletons lay buried in mud or sand, water circulating around them gradually dissolved their bone material, which was replaced with minerals. Now the "bones" are solid rock.

The fossils that we are able to discover are those lying near the surface. As a rule they are encased in broken mantle rock. Since the "bones" also may be weathered and fragile, the rock around them must be picked away carefully. As part of a fossil is uncovered, shellac is brushed over it to help hold it together. Then it is wrapped in burlap and plaster, hoisted out of the excavation, and crated for shipment.

The town of Ekalaka, Montana, considered itself fortunate when dinosaur fossils were discovered nearby. Men, women, and children joined the local geological society. Working under the guidance of experts, they helped to unearth and preserve the fossils. The picture on the right shows a group on their way to the dinosaur beds.

Photos: American Museum of Natural History; Roland T. Bird; Ross Madden, Black Star

150

UNEARTHING A DINOSAUR

ON THE LEFT, members of the Carter County Geological Society are at
work near Ekalaka, Montana, uncovering a dinosaur fossil. Above, they
pack it in plaster and burlap for shipment.

BRONTOSAURUS

During the jurassic, the climate of the interior of North America was tropical. Seas covered much of the continent. Around them spread vast marshlands, which were regularly drenched with rain, then lay steaming in the sun. Plants flourished in the wet warmth, crowding the swamps with their foliage.

For plant eaters, life was easy. Descendants of little, two-legged dinosaurs developed into huge creatures. While browsing in the swamps they propped themselves on their front limbs. Finally, the bigger herbivores became so heavy that they had to stay down on all fours. Yet it is clear that they were descended from two-legged ancestors, for in every one of them the hind legs were larger and stronger than the front, and carried the greater part of the animal's weight.

Brontosaurus, "thunder dinosaur," is well-known from skeletons like the one shown here, which is in the American Museum of Natural History in New York. The monster weighed about forty tons. It would have been an enormous task to carry that bulk around on land. Most of the time Brontosaurus waded, partly buoyed up by the water.

The creature's eyes were set high, and its nostrils opened through the top of its skull. This arrangement allowed it to see and breathe while almost completely submerged.

Brontosaurus had a small mouth to feed a big body. We can imagine that it passed most of its time gobbling down plants. But it was stodgy and wasted little energy moving around, which reduced the amount of food needed. Also helpful was the fact that Brontosaurus was "cold-blooded."

A modern warm-blooded animal spends energy in the form of heat to keep its body warmer than the surrounding air or water. Brontosaurus, however, simply cooled off when the temperature of the air or water fell. Instead of generating excess heat, it used most of its food to build and maintain its mountain of flesh and bone.

Photos: painting by Charles R. Knight, American Museum of Natural History (opposite); Arthur Lavine

WINGED REPTILES AND BIRDS

By the time of the early reptiles, many insects had become flyers, but no vertebrate had managed to lift itself into the air. It probably took millions of years for certain reptile lines to develop wings. Their ancestors, we imagine, were nimble creatures that scampered up tree trunks in order to escape enemies or chase insects. Perhaps a flap of skin spreading between the arm and body helped them to glide when they jumped to the ground.

By the close of the Triassic, descendants of the tree-climbers possessed wings. The little finger had lengthened greatly; from it and from the whole arm a web of skin stretched back to the body, forming a wing. The other three fingers, at the crook of the wing, were used for clinging.

The earliest kind of winged reptile was the size of a sparrow. A Jurassic type, shown in the picture at the left, grew as large as a crow. Judging from its build, it probably could not flap its wings easily. It must have been a glider rather than a true flyer. It could not take off from the ground, but launched itself from a tree or other high place. If it accidentally fell, it had to climb a tree in order to get into the air again.

During the rise of these reptiles, another line was evolving into the first birds. They are known from two fossils discovered in a limestone quarry near Solenhofen, Germany. In Jurassic times, the limey material was mud at the bottom of a lagoon. The two birds evidently drowned and sank into the mud. Their bones became fossilized, and even impressions of the feathers were preserved.

The ancient bird clearly was descended from reptiles. It had a reptilian jaw with teeth, a long reptilian tail, and claws on the wing bones. The feet, of the perching type, show that the bird came from a line of tree-climbers.

Photos: painting by Charles R. Knight, American Museum of Natural History (left); Gerhard Heilman, The Origin of Birds, 1926

SEA ROVERS

DURING THE 70 million years of the Cretaceous, ocean water twice submerged the interior of North America. The second and greater flood extended from Mexico to Alaska.

Giant reptiles roved the seas. Most terrible among them was the great mosasaur shown above; it grew to a length of 35 feet. The marine turtle Archelon was twelve feet wide across the front flippers.

The flying reptile Pteranodon rode the winds on wings spreading 25 feet. Its long beak was counterbalanced by a crest. This probably worked like the feather on an arrow, helping to keep the reptile's beak pointed forward as it flew.

The large fish Portheus is known from fossils dug out of chalk beds in Kansas. The pictures show a 14-foot specimen. This individual died soon after swallowing a six-foot Gillicus fish. The Gillicus was not even partly digested, so the two fishes, eater and eaten, became fossilized together.

Photos: painting by Charles R. Knight, Chicago Natural History Museum; Kansas State College Museum

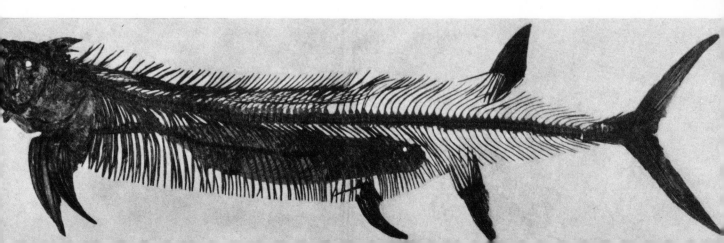

THE FIRST HORN-FACE

FOR A LONG WHILE scientists had supposed that dinosaurs laid eggs, but there was no proof. Then, in 1925, an expedition of the American Museum of Natural History, while exploring in the Mongolian Desert, discovered some nests of fossilized eggs. They were long, like the eggs of modern lizards, and the shells had a rough, pebbled surface.

In the same rock formation lay fossils of a queer little dinosaur about five feet long. It had a large skull with a heavy beak. The bones of the roof of the skull extended backward, forming a shield that covered the neck and shoulders. The creature had a bony knob on its face—not a true horn—yet it was easily recognized as a member of the group known as ceratopsians, "horn-faces." Like its relatives, it fed on plants.

Did Protoceratops ("first horn-face") lay the eggs found in the desert? Two of them, when examined, gave the answer. Inside them were the bones of little horn-faces, fossilized without ever having hatched.

Photos: American Museum of Natural History; painting by Charles R. Knight, Chicago Natural History Museum

BATTLE OF GIANTS

THE CRETACEOUS was a time for giants. Continental seas gave North America a bland, moist climate, which caused plants to spread as a green blanket over the land. Plant-eaters flourished in the garden of plenty, and flesh-eaters had abundant prey. Animals lived under conditions that remained almost the same for tens of millions of years. No great environmental changes weeded out unsuited types and selected others for survival. The main problem was competition among the various animal types themselves. In this situation, size and strength were advantageous; among successful lines, many became giants.

Among the ceratopsians, the giant was Triceratops, "Three-horned face." The monster stood seven feet high at the hips and was over twenty

feet long. Its skull, from the top of the beak to the flaring shield, measured over six feet. The brute carried two great horns over its eyes and one on its nose. A plant-eater, it roamed the North American lowlands, feeding on their lush vegetation.

Triceratops needed its weapons to defend itself against the two-legged carnivore, Tyrannosaurus. This hideous beast would stride along with its head twenty feet in the air, on the lookout for prey. When a victim was found, the "tyrant" pounced upon it and, pinning the creature under a clawed foot, attacked with its dagger-like teeth.

Triceratops had to be approached from the side or rear. If it managed to keep its great weapons pointed at the enemy, it could win the battle.

Photo: painting by Charles R. Knight, Chicago Natural History Museum

FALL OF THE DINOSAURS

THESE WERE SOME of the great reptiles that inhabited North America during the close of the Cretaceous. The duck-billed dinosaur on the right (Edmontosaurus) walked on its hind legs, but lowered itself on all fours while cropping rushes along the edges of streams. The crested dinosaur in the swamp (Parasaurolophus) had similar habits, as did the hooded one (Corythosaurus) in the background on the left.

The creature in the center background (Struthiomimus) kept the bird-like form of the early dinosaurs, but was huge compared to them. With its long neck and legs, and its small head and toothless beak, it must have resembled an ostrich. It ran swiftly in pursuit of small reptiles, and also ate fruit and other plant food. Quite the opposite extreme was the squatty reptile in the left foreground (Palaeoscincus). Too slow to escape an enemy, it was protected by an armor of bony plates and spikes.

162

Kings of the land, sea, and air for 150 million years, the great reptile lines, one after another, died out. We assume their fall was connected with changes in the world about them. As North America and other continents slowly rose, seas drained. Widespread areas became dry, with greater extremes of heat and cold. Rising mountain systems cut off wet winds from the sea and helped create deserts. In one region after another, marshes disappeared, causing scarcity of the kinds of vegetation that nourished the browsing dinosaurs. As the plant-eaters died out, the flesh-eaters starved.

Such changes in climate had little effect on the seas, yet the great marine reptiles perished along with the lords of the land. The causes of their extinction remain a mystery.

Photo: painting by Charles R. Knight, Chicago Natural History Museum

THE WARM-BLOODED

WHILE DINOSAURS ruled the land, certain tiny creatures scampered through brush and other hiding places. Their fossils show they were insect-eaters resembling modern shrews. So far as we know, these were the first mammals—creatures that fed their young from milk glands, or *mammae*. During the Cretaceous, there rose other types, among them the opossum shown here (Eodelphis).

What the early mammal lacked in strength, it made up in nimbleness. It was much quicker and smarter than a reptile. We assume this from the differences between modern reptiles and mammals. A mammal can be more lively than a reptile because its whole metabolism, or body chemistry, works faster. Food burns quickly in its cells, giving it energy for a very active life. Even while the mammal is resting, its rate of metabolism ordinarily doesn't fall below a certain high level. Some of its energy is spent in the form of heat, which keeps its body warm when the weather becomes cool.

How did the young of these new types of animals come into the world? Birds, also warm-blooded, continued the practice of laying eggs. The embryos developing in the eggs had to be kept warm—a problem which the birds solved by brooding the eggs. Some mammals, like the modern platypus, were egg-layers. But in most lines the female brooded the embryo right inside her body. There it was sheltered, snug and warm, until birth.

During the close of the Cretaceous, cooling climates handicapped the reptiles. Whenever the air temperature fell, they became chilled and sluggish. The mammals and birds were much better off. Their regulated metabolism gave them a climate of their own, inside their bodies. This no doubt helped them to survive cold that brought hardship and death to reptiles.

Photo: painting by F. L. Jaques, American Museum of Natural History

EARLY HOOFED MAMMALS

DURING THE EARLY CENOZOIC, mammals inherited the reptiles' old territories and spread to new ones. They divided into many lines, which became fit to live in various kinds of surroundings.

The dinosaurs had been specialists. Each type was adapted to a certain kind of home and could live in no other. It was either a vegetarian or a flesh-eater, and if the supply of its special food gave out, it starved. The early mammal, on the contrary, managed to get along in different sorts of places, and had a varied diet.

The animal in the picture on the left, Ectoconus, belonged to the condylarths, a group that inhabited North America about sixty million years ago. They ate plant food, and probably meat, too, when they could find it. They were squatty, with heavy legs and a long, thick tail. Their foot had five toes, each ending with a sort of small hoof.

166

Very much like these creatures in appearance were the creodonts, the flesh-eaters of the time. They ate plant food when meat was scarce. There was no carnivore like the wolf or lion, with teeth suited only for tearing flesh and shearing bone; nor any herbivore like the cow, with teeth shaped only for nipping and grinding leaves.

Along with the creodonts and condylarths, some strikingly different mammals have been found. The picture below represents one of these. Slim, trim, about the size of a terrier, the creature was a horse. Earliest known member of the line, it has been fittingly named Eohippus, "dawn horse." Its teeth proclaim it an eater of soft leaves. The front feet had four toes, the hind feet three. Each toe ended with a hoof. Since no recognizable ancestor of Eohippus has been found, we conclude that the line originated in some unknown region, and later migrated to North America.

Photos: paintings by J. C. Germann and Charles R. Knight, American Museum of Natural History

THE OLD AND THE NEW

Around 50 million years ago, during the early Eocene, widely differing kinds of hoofed animals roamed the forests and savannas of North America. Giant among them was the Uinta beast, named after the Uinta Mountains in Utah, where its fossils have been found. Bulky as a modern rhinoceros, it clumped around the woodlands munching leaves and occasionally fighting with its dagger-like tusks.

The Uinta beast had three pairs of bony knobs on its skull, but just a little space for a brain. It must have been slow and stupid, depending for safety on huge size rather than intelligence.

Quite different was Orohippus, the creature on the left-hand side of the picture. A horse about as big as a collie, it represented the newer types of herbivores. It was trim and nimble, and had a fairly large brain for its size.

Orohippus must have found it rather easy to elude the flesh-eaters of the time, which were clumsy, old-fashioned creodonts. There were no wolves nor lions. Ancestors of the dog and cat tribes were developing in other parts of the world, but had not yet arrived in North America.

Early types of rhinoceros were almost as small and agile as the horse. While old-fashioned tribes were dying off, rhinos and horses flourished and spread over the North American continent.

Photo: painting by Charles R. Knight,
Chicago Natural History Museum

LIFE ON THE GRASSLANDS

IN MIOCENE TIMES, around 25 million years ago, the Rocky Mountains were rising. Lowlands to the east of them were uplifted and became high plains. The mountains drained the westerly winds, causing the plains to become drier. Forests lacked enough rainfall to support them. Trees died out and were replaced by grasses.

The change of vegetation caused a crisis among plant-eaters. Those that dwelt in the forest were browsers, feeding only on soft leaves. Horses had small, low-crowned teeth, unsuited for chewing grasses, which contained gritty silica that would wear them down. Most lines of horses could not thrive on the new plants, and died out. But among a few, the teeth became higher-crowned. Moreover, the teeth grew continuously, re-

placing the loss from wear. In time these lines became eaters of grass. Camels and rhinos also evolved into grazers.

In the plains scene above, horses are seen foraging. Long-necked camels file along behind them. On the left are a pair of rhinos; on the right, a strange, clawed plant-eater, Moropus. In the foreground stand a group of Dinohyus, pig-like animals as big as bulls. One is using its great tusks to dig up a root. At times they fought with these weapons, whose marks are found on their skulls.

Horses became supremely well-adapted to life on the plains. In time their side toes disappeared, and they stood high on a lengthened middle toe and hoof. With their trim, long-legged bodies, they could outrun enemies, and could travel far in search of grass.

Photo: painting by Charles R. Knight, Chicago Natural History Museum

SOUTH AMERICAN MAMMALS

At the beginning of the Cenozoic, as at the present time, South America and North America were connected by a "bridge" of land. Over it the early mammals migrated from one continent to the other. As a result of intermingling, the populations of the two continents remained similar. Then the bridge sank, cutting off South America.

When new types of animals from Asia spread over North America, all but a few of them were stopped by the sea from reaching South America. Old-fashioned mammals were left unchallenged there; they thrived and continued developing in their own ways. During the course of tens of millions of years, many strange types arose, unlike creatures of North America or any other continent.

The picture above shows members of two groups that flourished in South America half a million years ago. The glyptodonts belonged to the

armadillo tribe. Giants among them grew to a length of twelve or fourteen feet. A dome made of bony plates encased the body. The powerful tail had armor of the same kind, enforced with knobs or spines. The type in the foreground carried a spiked knob at the end of its tail. It probably wagged the knob with deadly effect when an enemy was foolish enough to approach.

From the ground sloth line came the monster Megatherium. It was as bulky as an elephant. Its massive tail served as a prop while it stood gathering leaves from trees. For defense, the ground sloth relied on its size and great claws. During the Ice Age, when the bridge to North America was restored, both glyptodonts and ground sloths crossed over it. Their fossils have been found from Florida to California. One type of ground sloth ranged as far north as Alaska.

Photo: painting by Charles R. Knight, Chicago Natural History Museum

BEASTS OF THE TAR PITS

About 100,000 years ago, animals like these were buried alive in oil seeps near the site of Los Angeles. In their time, oil containing asphalt oozed up from rocks under this place, drenching the ground and making it sticky. Sometimes water lay on top, and animals came there to drink. When they stepped into the mire they were caught. Struggling to escape, they only sank deeper.

The struggles of a sinking camel, sloth, or horse attracted wolves and giant vultures. But they withdrew before the mighty saber-tooth, fearing the blade-like tusks that jutted from its upper jaw.

Saber-tooths themselves frequently were trapped and died with their prey. Vultures settled on the carcasses for a feast. Some ate so much that they could not fly away, and they too foundered. Skeletons of these various animals were well preserved in the asphalt. Thousands have been dug up, and now stand on display in museums.

Photos: painting by Charles R. Knight, Chicago Natural History Museum; courtesy Los Angeles County Museum

THE TUNDRA AND ITS CREATURES

FROM 100,000 TO 25,000 years ago, ice sheets buried the northern regions of Europe, Asia, and North America. Cold winds blew outward around the ice, creating an arctic type of climate. Forests and most grasses disappeared. In their place grew cold-loving lichens, mosses, sedges, and heather. Such plants covered a zone of frigid plain—the tundra—which spread across central Europe, Asia, and North America. It was inhabited by the reindeer, musk ox, woolly mammoth, woolly rhinoceros, and other creatures that had become adapted to the climate and the plant food.

The last of the woolly mammoths lived on in the Arctic until a few thousand years ago. Some were trapped in quicksand, which froze and preserved their bodies. Remains of a baby woolly mammoth, shown on the right, were dug from a frozen sandbank in Alaska.

Photos: painting by Charles R. Knight, Chicago Natural History Museum; American Museum of Natural History

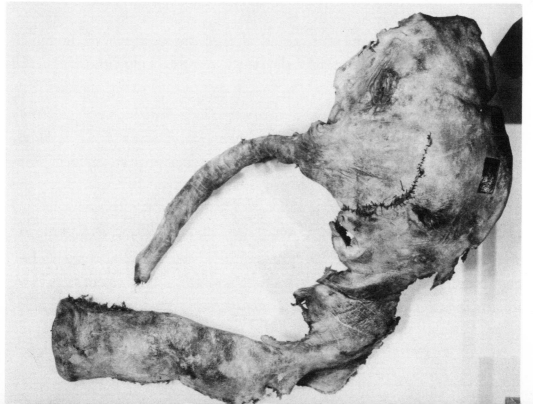

MAN, THE HUNTER

THOUGH WE HAVE LEARNED a good deal about the evolution of the horse, the elephant, and other animal lines, we know relatively little about the evolution of our own kind. Human fossils are rare, perhaps because man was intelligent enough to avoid the traps into which other creatures blundered and were fossilized. Only fragments of skulls and jawbones, rather apelike in form, provide evidence that types of man lived in Asia and Europe a few hundred thousand years ago.

When the third ice flood was receding, about 150,000 years ago, a race of hunters appeared in Europe. We know of them from skeletons preserved in caves where they took shelter. Neanderthal man, named after the district in Germany where his remains were first discovered, was squatty in build, but not small. As reconstructed in the scene shown above, he had a barrel chest and strong arms. His large head jutted forward from a short, thick neck. Bones of reindeer, bison, and horses have been found with Neanderthal remains, showing that the people hunted big game.

Skill at hunting and fishing enabled man to populate wide regions of the earth. During the close of the last glacial period, from 50,000 to 20,000 year ago, groups of people entirely modern in build were wandering into Europe from Asia and Africa. At times they camped in caves, and some of them decorated the cave walls with magnificent paintings of the beasts they hunted. The bison drawing shown here was copied from the famous cave of Altamira, in Spain.

As the last European ice sheet was retreating, the tundra zone shifted northward. The reindeer, the woolly mammoth, and the musk ox slowly

migrated to the Arctic, in this way remaining in their own kind of home, where they continued to feed on lichens and other cold-loving plants.

Where the great game herds went, human hunters followed. Their migration lasted many centuries. About 15,000 years ago, bands of them reached the northeast tip of Asia. At that time Bering Strait was narrow and shallow. Islands formed a chain across the water; in winter they were connected by ice.

The hunters looked across the Strait and saw, dimly outlined on the horizon, a far, strange land. They wondered if hunting was good there, made up their minds to explore the unknown country, and set off across the ice. When they stepped ashore on the other side they saw game, but no people. It was truly a new world, for until then no human being, so far as we know, had ever set foot upon North America. The discoverers, who were ancestors of the Indians, migrated along the river valleys and the shores. Their descendants spread through the woodlands, reached the plains, and populated most of the continent.

Photos: Chicago Natural History Museum; American Museum of Natural History

TREASURES
OF OUR
PLANET

TREASURES OF OUR PLANET

PREHISTORIC HUNTERS discovered ways of cultivating plants and keeping animals. These occupations enabled them to settle in permanent villages. They investigated the rocks about them, discovered metals, and learned to fashion metal tools.

Civilized man has enlarged upon these skills. From metals, he has devised machines for industry, and has built ships, railroads, and planes that carry products to all parts of the world. From rocks, he has taken fuels to power factories and engines of transportation.

The following pictures show how some of the raw materials of civilization are found and taken from the earth.

Photo: courtesy Standard Oil Company (New Jersey)

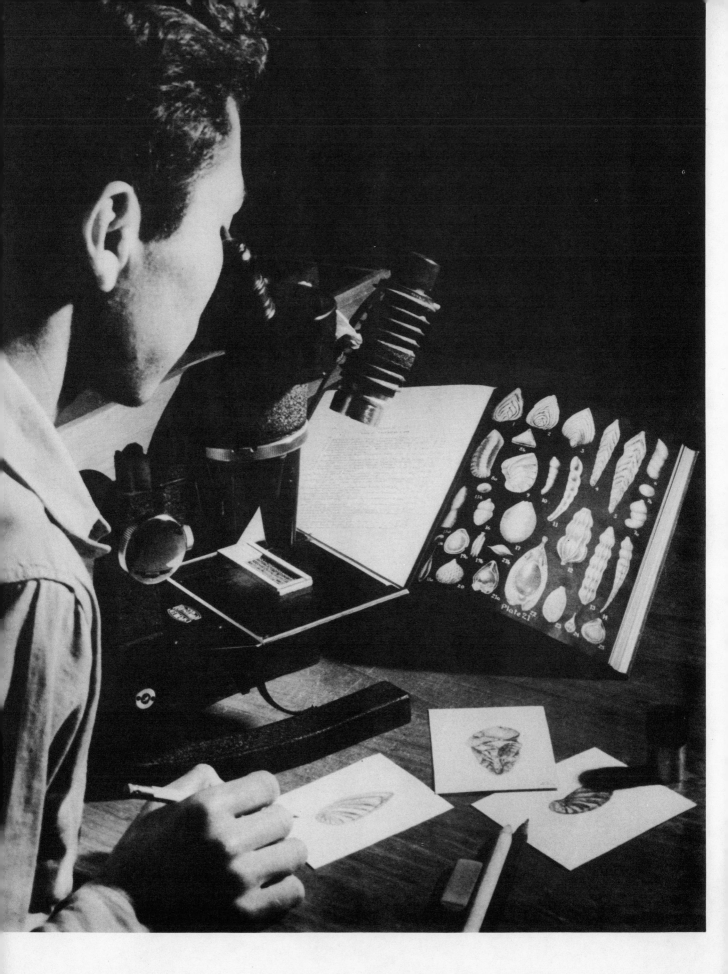

PETROLEUM—ITS ORIGIN

PETROLEUM, "oil from rock," is the main fuel of civilization today. It drives the engines of ships, planes, automobiles, trains. It yields power for factories and heat for homes. Materials derived from it are used in the manufacture of rubber tires, plastics, cosmetics, and many other products.

This treasure was created tens or hundreds of millions of years ago, from the body substances of creatures of the sea. In the past, as now, the ocean harbored a vast population of microscopic plants and animals. Hordes of them sank to the sea floor and were buried in mud. In time the mud became rock, and materials of the enclosed bodies became petroleum.

Shells of microscopic marine animals are shown below. On the left, an expert studies fossils from a rock boring. They may be a sign of oil.

Photos: courtesy Standard Oil Company (New Jersey)

OIL TRAPS

GEOLOGISTS KNOW they can expect to find oil only in areas covered by marine rocks. But such areas are vast, and oil deposits do not exist under them everywhere. Wildcatters, who depend on hunches in choosing places to drill, seldom strike oil. Just where, then, are stores of oil to be sought?

During early stages in its history, petroleum is spread very thinly through marine shales. Later, events in the crust may cause it to concentrate in certain places.

The model below illustrates a common type of structure where oil is found. The rock beds here have warped into folds. At the surface are outcrops of tilted layers which, if they were complete, would meet to form an arch. This indicates that the underlying rocks are curved into an arching fold—an anticline. The picture on the left shows an outcrop that helped geologists to locate the Lander Anticline, in Wyoming.

At the imaginary place shown in the model, petroleum had formed in beds of shale. As the shale compacted under pressure, the oil was squeezed out of it and seeped into neighboring layers of sandstone, which had more pore space between the grains.

An oil-bearing sandstone layer also contained gases and water. As the beds arched, the water settled down the arch, while oil and gases, being lighter, rose. They were trapped in the sandstone by impervious shale lying above and below it. Gradually, the sandstone at the crest of the fold became charged with oil and gas.

Photos: courtesy Standard Oil Company (New Jersey); American Museum of Natural History

THE QUEST FOR OIL

Several methods are used to locate oil traps. One is magnetic surveying. A magnetometer is towed through water, or through the air, as in the picture opposite. The "Maggie" records differences in the magnetic properties of rocks over which it passes. From the readings, geologists obtain clues about places that may be worth exploring.

The men in the picture below are using a gravity meter, which is a delicate spring instrument that measures the pull of gravity. Where the pull increases, it is a sign that deep, dense rocks approach the surface, as they do in the crest of an anticline.

Photos: courtesy Standard Oil Company (New Jersey); American Petroleum Institute

SEISMIC PROSPECTING

KNOWLEDGE GAINED from the study of earthquakes has been put to use in prospecting for oil. The procedure is to sink a charge of dynamite in bedrock and fire it, causing a miniature earthquake. Vibrations run through the rock, hit underlying structures, and are reflected. Detectors set at various points receive the reflected waves and transmit signals to recording instruments in a truck. Sometimes shots are fired under lakes or offshore waters, or in swamps, if the rock formations seem worth investigating.

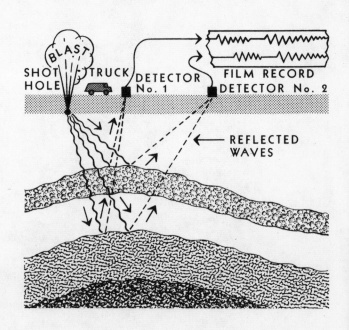

From the seismographic records, geologists are able to locate any promising structure under the surface. The elapsed time between a shot and the arrival of reflected waves tells the distance the waves have traveled—in other words, the depth of the reflecting structure. Its shape is defined by a whole set of records.

When an anticline crest or other possible trap has been located, it is time for the final test—drilling. If the shaft strikes a bed of reservoir rock, the pressure of gas and water in it may be strong enough to send oil gushing to the surface.

Photos: courtesy Standard Oil Company (New Jersey); American Petroleum Institute

COAL: FOSSIL SUNLIGHT

WHEN WE BURN COAL, we use sunlight that reached the earth around 250 million years ago. At that time North America was low, and much of it was covered by an inland sea. Around the sea lay broad marshlands, overgrown with forests of giant rushes and ferns like those in the picture. Their leaves trapped energy from sunlight, which was used in the making of food. The food provided material for growth.

Dead trees and branches fell into swamp water, where they were protected from air and the bacteria that cause decay. The plant material did not rot away, but changed into the dark, spongy stuff called peat.

From time to time the ground sank, and the swamps with their plant remains were covered by the sea. As layers of mud piled on top of the peat, pressure transformed it into lignite, a low-grade coal. The load of sediments grew, pressure increased, and the lignite turned into soft (bituminous) coal. In some places, coal beds were involved in folding and uplift that produced mountain ranges. During the process, the soft coal turned into hard (anthracite) coal.

Plant parts in the coal itself have been crushed into an unrecognizable mass. But fossils are preserved in shale lying next to coal seams. Some molds and imprints reproduce whole plants. In the fossil at the right, the veins and texture of the leaves are preserved clearly.

Millions of tons of coal are mined each year, mostly by men operating power-driven machines. The picture below shows a "mechanical crocodile" that can scoop up four tons of coal a minute. Using machines such as this, miners can supply us with all the coal we need.

Today "fossil sunlight" serves us both as a fuel and a chemical raw material. Substances derived from coal are used for making dyes, artificial flavors, plastics, nylon, explosive, medicines, and many other products.

Photos: Chicago Natural History Museum; courtesy National Coal Association

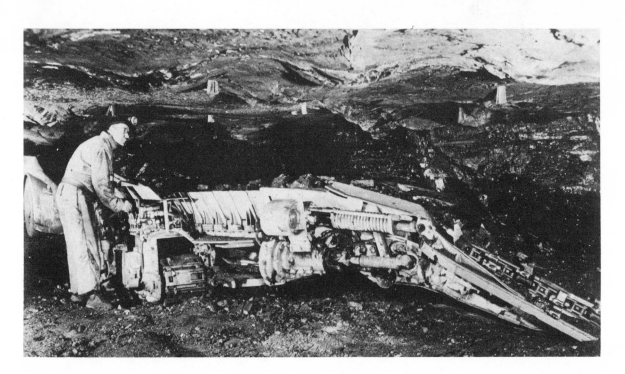

URANIUM FOR ENERGY

CIVILIZATION NEEDS NEW SOURCES of energy. If man were to go on burning coal and oil at the present rate, the world's known reserves would be used up in a few centuries. The outlook is brightened by the achievements of nuclear scientists, who have probed the atom and managed to tap some of its stored-up energy.

Uranium, the principal atomic fuel up to the present, is scattered in minute amounts through rocks of the crust. Decaying slowly, uranium and other radioactive elements have supplied the heat of magmas. Rocks derived from magmas contain traces of uranium. Ordinary granites have enough to be worth extracting, should other sources fail.

There seems to be no danger of this happening for a long while, since new, rich mines are being opened in Ontario and other places. Such supplies probably spell the end of the recent "uranium rush." Amateur prospectors, like the man in the picture, will go back to fishing and other sports.

Photos: courtesy Mining World; Standard Oil Company (New Jersey)

SALT OF THE EARTH

IN SOME PARTS of the world people obtain salt from sea water, which they evaporate in large pans. When some brine has evaporated completely, a deposit of white crystals is left on the bottom of the pan. Most of the crystals are common table salt (sodium chloride), but in addition there are other salts, bitter and useless for seasoning. The evaporation process must be controlled very painstakingly in order to get table salt pure enough for use.

Salt-making by evaporation has gone on in nature on a large scale. Over 350 million years ago a sea was cut off in the region of western New York and the Great Lakes, which then had a dry climate. As the sea shrank from evaporation, brine remained in a number of basins, and sodium chloride precipitated and settled over their floors. Later, the salt was covered with layers of sand and mud. These consolidated into sandstone and shale, and the salt too was transformed into rock.

Being pure sodium chloride, rock salt is worth some effort to obtain. According to one method, a well is drilled down to the vein and filled with water, then the brine is pumped up and evaporated. Salt is also mined in solid form. One mine spreads under Detroit like a city beneath a city.

A deep vein of salt is under great pressure. Sometimes the pressure becomes diminished at a certain place, as when material is eroded from the surface. Greater pressure elsewhere squeezes the salt upward where pressure is less. It forms a plug that punches through overlying rock beds and may lift the surface into a dome. The picture shows a mine chamber in a plug of salt at Avery Island, Louisiana.

Photo: courtesy International Salt Company

RUST AS IRON ORE

IRON, THE KEY METAL of civilization, lies under our feet everywhere—not as a free element, but in combination with others. Its atoms are built into the crystals of many common minerals. Iron makes up, on the average, five per cent of the weight of igneous rocks. When the rocks weather, the iron unites with oxygen and water to form iron oxides. These are the compounds of ordinary rust. They often color a weathered rock face tawny or pink, though the rock is gray when freshly broken. Soils derived from such rocks are yellow or red from the rust in them.

Some iron could be extracted from most rocks and soils, but the job would be too costly. To be usable as ore, a material must have a metal content of 25 percent or more, which is unusual. Iron is well distributed among minerals of the crust, and some geological process is necessary to select and concentrate it. In some cases, minerals rich in iron have gathered by settling out of a magma. More often, they have been concentrated through processes operating at the surface.

Iron deposits around Lake Superior were formed by sedimentation at the bottom of an ancient sea. Later, the iron-bearing rocks were exposed and weathered. A great deal of silica washed out of the rock waste, leaving the iron concentrated in the form of hematite, a mineral made of the oxide that forms rust. At the Mesabi Range, the ore is so loose that it is shoveled from open pits without blasting. Millions of tons have been removed during the last hundred years. Now the best ores are near exhaustion, and deposits in South America have begun to take their place. The pictures show mining at Cerro Bolívar, in Venezuela.

Photos: courtesy United States Steel Corporation

ALUMINUM

THE ELEMENT ALUMINUM, though never found free in nature, is as common as dirt. Ordinary clay is made of aluminum silicates—combinations of aluminum with silicon, oxygen, and water. The clay minerals come from the weathering of feldspars in igneous rocks. These rocks have an average aluminum content of more than eight percent, which means that the earth's crust is one-twelfth aluminum.

Nearly twice as abundant as iron, aluminum is less frequently concentrated in usable ores. This is because the clay minerals seldom break down, and aluminum remains bound in the silicates.

In the tropics, factors of climate sometimes produce ground water solutions that slowly dissolve silica out of clay, leaving aluminum oxide. When the content is 50 percent or more, the deposit can be used as an ore. It is called bauxite after the town of Les Baux in southern France, where deposits were originally found.

Large quantities of bauxite are mined in Arkansas, and also in British Guiana and Surinam (Dutch Guiana). The usual method is open-pit or "strip" mining, but sometimes ore is taken from underground diggings, as shown in the picture opposite. In the scene below, from Surinam, a crew is drilling holes for dynamite blasting.

Photos: courtesy Aluminum Company of America

COPPER

MANY MINERAL DEPOSITS can be traced to the activity of magmas. Sometimes a magma shoves between rock layers, separating them and thus making a chamber with a floor and roof. As the magma cools, its substances link to form crystals. Denser minerals, with a large content of heavy metal atoms, sink and collect near the floor. Some of the copper and nickel deposits of Norway and Canada were formed in this way.

As a magma becomes more and more solid, leftover gases and liquids are forced out of it, escaping through cracks in the roof of the magma chamber. Compounds of copper, nickel, gold, silver, lead, zinc, and iron may be carried in the fluids. As they seep upward, the fluids remove rock from the walls of the fissures, replacing it with metals and metal compounds. Remnants of the metals reach the surface through volcanoes, hot springs, and fumaroles (gas vents). At deep levels, they are deposited as sulphides—compounds of sulphur.

Copper sulphide that originated in this way is mined from Bingham Canyon, Utah, shown in the picture above. The scene at the right shows part of the copper mines at Cerro de Pasco in the Peruvian Andes.

Photos: courtesy Copper & Brass Research Association; Grace Line

WATER

O<small>F ALL THE EARTH'S TREASURES</small>, water is the most familiar and yet the most unusual. Our neighbor planets, Mercury, Venus, and Mars, have little or none. Undoubtedly they once possessed a fair supply, but lost it because their weak gravity allowed water vapor and other gases to drift away. Remnants of water, if they exist, are mostly bound up in the rocks.

The earth too, during its creation, lost water vapor along with other gases. Some water, however, was preserved in the rocks. When the interior grew hot from radioactivity, magmas formed, and volcanoes belched out clouds of steam. Rain drenched the face of the planet. Water flooded through rivers into the great basins. The ocean formed; in time it was to become the cradle of life.

In passing through soil and over rock, water dissolves the substances needed for plant growth. From plants, animals of the land and sea derive the precious materials of life. Foods are carried in a watery solution through the bodies of all creatures, and indeed the body tissues themselves are largely water.

The liquid of life is the first need of any community. To provide water in abundance, engineers have built great dams, canals, and pipe systems. Government surveyors measure snow in the mountains in order to estimate the future water supply and plan its use. Water, the medium of life, is the first raw material of civilization.

Photos: Ewing Galloway; courtesy Union Pacific Railroad (above)

TIME AND MAN

So far as scientists can estimate, the earth has existed for about 5,000 million years. The first living things may have originated 2,000 million years ago, but the fossil record is clear only for the last 500 million years. And only in the last moment of geological time—only about a million years ago—man appeared.

Man resembles other animals in the way his body functions, but he has a talent that places him above them all. This is intelligent co-operation. He speaks with his fellows; together they work and learn; together they create things that no man could create alone.

Through co-operation, men have learned to cultivate plants instead of gathering them, and to breed animals instead of hunting them. With metals taken from the earth, men have fashioned machines to multiply the work of their hands. They have tapped the energy of rivers, coal, oil, and the atom, and have used this energy to drive the engines of civilization.

We all share the treasures of the earth, as we share the treasures of human knowledge and art; and we enjoy them because they are shared. This is the heritage of man—intelligent co-operation to master the earth, and to share its bounties.

Part Five ⁊ ⁊ ⁊

GUIDES
TO
DISCOVERY

GUIDES TO DISCOVERY

EXCITING ADVENTURES are in store for all who set out to read the earth's story in the field. Any place is a good place to start. Every region has a geological past, which is recorded in its hills, valleys, and plains, and in its soil and rock. In many places the rocks contain beautiful minerals; in others, fascinating fossils.

No special gadgets are needed for exploration. The main tool is an acquaintance with earth science.

Many government agencies and museums are prepared to help the amateur geologist. These organizations will answer questions and aid in identifying specimens. They also publish inexpensive field guides, reports, and maps.

By use of such resources it is possible to interpret local geological features and trace their history. There are several kinds of materials and services that will be helpful.

GENERAL REFERENCE BOOKS

BOOKS ON THE different branches of earth science can be obtained from most libraries. Examine them, and when you find one suited to your needs, you may order it from the publisher or a local bookstore.

A good plan for the beginner is to read the books for young people first, and work up to those that are more advanced. Many of the junior books on geological subjects suggest activities related to field work. Some give directions on how to start a rock and mineral collection.

A handbook for identifying rocks and minerals is a necessity in field work. This type of book is made pocket-sized, to be carried out of doors. There is no popular guide to fossils. Those interested in fossil identification may use a standard textbook on historical geology, then go on to specialized handbooks.

An excellent book list, called *The Earth for the Layman,* has been prepared by the American Geological Institute. It includes books for children, field guides, textbooks, and non-technical state reports. It costs $1.00, and may be ordered from the National Research Council, 2101 Constitution Avenue, Washington 25, D. C.

Photo: courtesy Union Pacific Railroad

REGIONAL GUIDES AND MAPS

GOVERNMENT AGENCIES publish a great deal of material dealing with particular regions and localities. Every state of the United States, and every province of Canada, has a geological survey or bureau of mines and resources which studies and maps its own area. Survey headquarters are in capital cities. A state geologist or director is in charge. Inquiries on publications, as well as questions about local features and specimens, should be addressed to him.

Each state and provincial survey sends free on request a price list of its guides, bulletins, and maps. Many of these publications are technical, but some are popular. Titles usually indicate the level of difficulty.

A beginner should not hesitate to use publications for specialists if they apply to his own neighborhood. They may be the only ones that describe and explain local features.

Both in the United States and in Canada, the federal government conducts geological surveys. Most reports deal with specific areas. For a price list of these publications write to:

Superintendent of Documents,
  U.S. Government Printing Office, Washington 25, D.C.
Geological Survey of Canada, Ottawa, Canada.

Of especial value are the topographic and geological maps of local areas. The topographic maps show landscape features, trails, mines, and quarries. They are useful in planning field trips. The geological maps show the formations of the regional bedrock. Both types of maps can be obtained from the national surveys. Many state and provincial surveys sell them, too. Request a key sheet which lists topographic and geological maps for the area you wish to study, then order those you need. The cost is nominal.

You may also find regional reports and maps at a public or school library. If they are not in the collection, the librarian probably will be glad to obtain them.

Photos: courtesy Ward's Natural Science Establishment

NATIONAL, STATE, AND PROVINCIAL PARKS

SOME OF THE most interesting areas in the United States and Canada have been set aside as parks. Some are national parks; others are state or provincial parks. The National Park Service of the United States has prepared a number of booklets describing geological and other features of the various parks. You may write to the Superintendent of Documents in Washington for a checklist of the National Park Service publications, and for a small fee obtain the ones that interest you. For information on Canadian parks, write to the Minister of Resources and Development, Ottawa, Canada.

When planning to visit a national park, it is a good idea to read the booklet about that park. Then you will be well prepared to understand its geological and other features.

MUSEUM SERVICES

EVERY NATURAL HISTORY museum has a department of geology and mineralogy. The staff members do research, prepare displays, and publish reports on the geology of the surrounding areas. They are glad to answer inquiries and assist in identifying specimens.

When possible, visit the nearest museum having a collection of minerals, rocks, and fossils. Labels usually tell where the specimens were obtained. It is a good idea to note the source areas nearby. Very likely, similar specimens can be found at these sites. Directions for locating them may be obtained from the staff.

A number of museums circulate loan collections of minerals and rocks to schools and organizations. They also circulate motion pictures on geological and other subjects. As a rule, these services are offered by the museum educational division.

In addition, several of the larger museums have a bookshop that sells local field guides and selected books. They are prepared to fill orders by mail.

Photo: courtesy National Park Service

MINERAL COLLECTORS' CLUBS

THOUSANDS OF amateur mineralogists go prospecting as a hobby. Many belong to clubs that take regular field trips. Hundreds of these clubs are scattered through the United States and Canada. They welcome guests and new members. A great many of them have junior memberships for young people.

Some clubs study fossils as well as minerals. Under competent guidance, they collect and prepare specimens for display. Anyone interested in fossil hunting should join one of these groups. Individual collecting is inadvisable, for it may lead to the destruction of precious relics of the past.

For information about local clubs, write to the geology department of the nearest natural history museum, or to the director of your geological survey.

MAGAZINES FOR HOBBYISTS

NEWS OF MINERALOGICAL club activities, field work suggestions, and popular articles on geology can be found in these periodicals:

Rocks and Minerals. Editor, Peter Zodac; published bimonthly at Box 29, Peekskill, New York. Subscription, $3.00 a year.

Earth Science. Editor, Dr. Ben H. Wilson; published monthly at Box 1357, Chicago 90, Illinois. Subscription, $2.00 a year.

The Mineralogist. Editor, Dr. H. C. Drake; published monthly, except in summer, at 329 S.E. 32nd Ave., Portland 15, Oregon. Subscription, $2.00 a year.

In addition, there are several specialized magazines for gem collectors. There are also regional magazines. Information about these can be obtained from local clubs, museums, or libraries.

Photos: courtesy Mineralogical Society of Pennsylvania, by Harold Evans (opposite); Ward's Natural Science Establishment

FIELD EQUIPMENT

THE LARGEST AND oldest geological supply house in the United States is Ward's Natural Science Establishment, P. O. Box 24, Beechwood Station, Rochester 9, New York. This organization serves hobbyists as well as professional geologists, schools, and museums. A complete list of dealers is available in the *Rockhound Buyer's Guide,* published annually. The price is $2.00. To order, write to Box 518, Del Mar, California.

For most types of exploring and collecting, very little equipment is needed. The less one carries, the better. Rockhounds usually take only these items:

A pocket magnifying glass for mineral study.

A stone mason's or a geologist's hammer, and a small cold chisel, for breaking samples of rock. A stone mason's hammer and chisel can be purchased at a hardware store; a geologist's hammer, from a supply house. The geologist's hammer is more expensive.

A small knapsack for specimens; and maps, a field guide, and a notebook.

These tools are helpful, but more important is knowing what to look for. Geological wonders are everywhere, awaiting discovery.

Photos: courtesy Ward's Natural Science Establishment

INDEX

Index

Index (continued)